THE CHALLENGE
OF THE SPACE AGE

the

CHALLENGE

of the

SPACE AGE

JOHN W. KLOTZ

Professor of Natural Science
Concordia Senior College
Fort Wayne, Indiana

Concordia Publishing House • Saint Louis

Concordia Publishing House, Saint Louis 18, Missouri

Concordia Publishing House Ltd., London, W. C. 1

Copyright 1961 by Concordia Publishing House

Library of Congress Catalog Card No. 61-13456

Manufactured in the United States of America

CONTENTS

PREFACE

Twentieth-century living is a complicated thing. The simplicity of past generations has gone. We look with nostalgia to the "good old days," when life seemed so much calmer and quieter. The leisurely pace of quiet village life, the Sunday afternoon band concerts, the old swimming hole, the clomp of horses' hoofs on the dusty road, the general store are all a thing of the past. Instead we have apartment living, subways, jets, supermarkets, physical fitness classes at the YMCA — and with them tranquilizers and sleeping pills.

If only we could turn back the clock! But time will not stand still. Those days are gone and gone forever.

And so we look for a scapegoat, someone or something to blame for our present situation. What is it that has changed our lives? What is it that has made them so complicated? What is it that has catapulted us into the space age? This is the age of science. It would seem that science is responsible, and there are many who wonder whether in science we have not created a Frankenstein monster.

But before deciding to discard science or perhaps to declare at least a moratorium on scientific study and research, perhaps we first ought to stop to determine whether we really want to go back to the "good old days." There was indeed peace and tranquillity, but there was also much more. There was also dirt and disease. There was grinding poverty, poor housing, hard physical labor. From some of these a few could find escape, just as there are still some Americans today who must suffer grinding poverty and must be content with substandard housing. But even the wealthy could not escape the dirt and disease of the day. A large bank account was a poor defense against smallpox, the plague, and dysentery. Perhaps the "good old days" were not as good as they seemed!

Man has always had his problems. The space age is not new in that it presents some. But man has usually learned to rise above them by regarding them as challenges. So it is in this space age. There are indeed problems. It would be unwise to ignore them, to view life only through rose-colored glasses. But rather than bemoan these problems we ought to regard them as challenges. It is from this perspective that we want to view the scientific advances of our age.

Fort Wayne, Indiana   John W. Klotz

SCIENCE COMES OF AGE

chapter

1

SCIENCE COMES
OF AGE

One of the most important agents of God in bringing blessings to those living in the middle of the 20th century has been the scientist. Through his hands the windows of heaven have been opened and God's gifts have rained on us in abundance. Luxury, leisure, and ease are so much a part of our life that we take them for granted. We have a standard of living higher than ever before in the world's history. The average American of 1776 had the help of one servant for two weeks a year; today through the energy harnessed by the scientist he has the equivalent of 60 servants all year round. We have been relieved of almost all toil and drudgery. Our work is done for us by machines. No longer are we dependent on the energy released by human muscles and the muscles of animals, the source of energy in ancient civilizations and societies. This dependence made slavery almost a necessity. It made a middle class unthinkable. There could be only the exploited and exploiters. Society had to be organized as a pyramid, with many on the bottom and few on the top. Only a few men could be wealthy. Only a few men could enjoy luxury and ease. The privileges of the wealthy were possible only because the masses were poor.

Then the scientist succeeded in harnessing the energy God had placed in coal, and it became available to human beings. The Industrial Revolution was the result. England became a wealthy nation because she had large coal deposits and quickly learned how to utilize them. About 100 years ago the energy of petroleum was offered to us after the drilling of the first commercial oil well by Col. Drake at Titusville, Pa., in 1859. Then in the years following World War II natural gas became widely available as long-distance transportation of the fuel by pipeline became feasible.

The scientist has also made living itself more agreeable. He has conquered many of the scourges which once swept through nations and even continents. Bubonic plague is a thing of the past. Smallpox no longer sweeps like a shadow over the continents. Many an irrevocable death sentence has now been revoked. Even 50 years ago a diagnosis of pernicious anemia or of diabetes was a sentence of death. Today this is no longer true. These disorders are in most cases only nuisances. As a consequence life expectancies have moved steadily upward. In colonial America a baby could expect to live but 30 years; today a newborn American can look forward to a life expectancy of 69.3 years that are relatively free from sickness.

Scientists have also met the challenge of increasing populations in the United States. While it is true that in many lands there is a real population problem, this is not the case in the United States. Our population has increased substantially, particularly in the years since World War II, but our ability to produce food has increased even faster. The problem in the United States is not shortages but surpluses. In spite of efforts to decrease food production and limit it, more food is being produced than ever before. By selective breeding better crop plants have been developed. More wheat and more corn are being produced on fewer acres. Animal husbandry has also moved forward. For instance, it now takes fewer pounds of corn to get a hog ready for market.

All of this has represented a tremendous step forward. We are living better than ever before. And these things have come through the research of scientists. They have been God's agents in showering down these blessings on us.

Because of this progress we are becoming increasingly aware of the important role science has in our society. Our civilization could not have arisen without science, basic and applied, and it could not long continue without it. We owe a tremendous debt to our scientists. We ought to be thankful to God for the blessings they have brought us.

But science does not stand still. Science continues to move forward. One research project builds upon another. Scientific progress moves at an ever-quickening pace. It is likely that this will continue. It is probable that science will move forward at what might be called a geometric rate. Today science has a broader base than ever before. There are more and more bits of research to build on. The result is that we may expect to move forward even faster in the future than we have in the past.

Yet rapid progress in itself is not always good. For whenever new sources of energy are released, problems arise. The Industrial Revolution brought economic dislocation and social problems. There were those who wanted to exploit this new source of energy only for their own personal benefit. They wanted to take advantage of it for themselves. The new machines made child labor and sweatshops feasible. In addition, serious economic dislocations resulted when machines were substituted for men.

We are faced with both economic dislocation and social problems once more today as we stand on the threshold of a second Industrial Revolution. This is deeply disturbing. There are some thinking men who call for a moratorium on science. They believe that progress has outstripped our ability to integrate this progress with our social structure and to deal with its consequences. They feel that the natural sciences should halt until the social sciences catch up. It is this feeling that leads to many of the tensions of our age and to the general nervousness and jitteryness that characterize it.

Atomic Energy

Let us look at one of these areas of scientific development and study its problems. Progress has been rapid in the past years in the area of harnessing and releasing new sources of energy. We are no longer completely dependent on coal, oil, and natural gas. The scientist has succeeded in harnessing the atom and in releasing its energy. God has placed a tremendous amount of energy in the atom. It is estimated that if we could release all of the energy from a gram — 1/28th ounce — of matter, we would have the energy equivalent of 23,000 tons of coal. To be sure we shall never release all this energy. Our most efficient coal or oil burning engines release less than half the fuel energy. Yet if we release only a small part of the energy of the atom we shall have become immensely wealthy. And we are moving ahead to the use of a part of the energy of the atom. Already from a cubic inch of uranium which weighs about a pound we can release the energy equivalent of 1,500 tons of coal or of 250,000 gallons of diesel oil.

Fission Processes

Actually there are two processes by which the energy of the atom may be released. The first of these is through a process of fission. According to this process the atom is split. A heavy atom is broken down into simpler atoms, and some of the original mass is changed into energy. That this would occur was first suggested by two German physicists, Otto Hahn and F. Strassmann, on January 6, 1939, shortly before the outbreak of World War II. They reported that barium, lanthanum, cerium, and krypton seemed to be present in substances containing uranium which had been exposed to neutrons, one of the particles from which atoms are made. Within two months more than 40 papers were published on the fission of uranium. The most significant thing about the discovery was not that atoms could be split but rather the tremendous amount of energy released in the process. It was noted that when uranium split, the weight of the products did not equal the original weight of the uranium. Part of this loss in weight was represented by the energy released and part by free neutrons. These free neutrons were capable of initiating fission in other uranium atoms. Since more than one neutron was released at each fission, the number of free neutrons and the number of fissioning nuclei increased rapidly with each fission.

Uranium is of several isotopes which differ in their atomic weights. It was discovered that the most common form of uranium, that with a weight of 238 and designated U^{238}, does not readily undergo fission. U^{235}, which constitutes about 0.71% of all uranium, is the actual isotope of uranium which undergoes fission. However, when U^{238} is bombarded with neutrons, it is changed into another isotope of uranium, U^{239}. This transformation can be accomplished only if the neutrons are not traveling too fast. Those released from U^{235} have a speed far too great for them to be absorbed by and react with U^{238}. If, however, these can be slowed down, they may be made to react with the U^{238} to form U^{239}.

U^{239} is itself radioactive. It ejects a beta particle to form element 93, neptunium. U^{239} has a half life of only 23 minutes. In that time half a given quantity of the element has broken down. Hence uranium that is bombarded with slow neutrons is quickly converted into neptunium. Neptunium is in turn radioactive. It has a half life of 2.3 days. It emits a beta particle and is changed into element 94, plutonium, one of the important elements used in fission processes.

Plutonium is usually prepared from pure uranium which contains about 0.71% U^{235}. The U^{238} present acts to dilute the U^{235} and to prevent an explosion. The U^{235} undergoes spontaneous fission. The process is hastened by preventing the escape of the neutrons. The neutrons ejected by the U^{235} are slowed down by some light element such as heavy hydrogen, carbon in the form of graphite, or beryllium. These slow neutrons act on the U^{238} to change it eventually to plutonium.

Either plutonium or U^{235} which has been separated from the U^{238} may be used as a source of energy. Both undergo fission with an attendant expulsion of neutrons. These expelled neutrons can cause fission in more atoms. If each uranium or plutonium atom undergoing fission gives off enough neutrons to cause fission in more than one atom, a large scale explosion results. This is the principle behind the atomic bomb. There is a certain critical mass which must be reached before an explosion can take place. A small lump of either U^{235} or plutonium does not explode because some neutrons are lost and some react with impurities. But if the mass is greater than a certain critical point, there will be sufficient fission to cause an explosion. Accordingly a bomb is made of two masses of U^{235} or plutonium, neither of which is large enough to cause an explosion. These are kept apart until the moment of the explosion arrives. Then the two lumps are quickly brought together. Their combined mass exceeds the critical mass, and an atomic explosion results.

U^{233}, which is made from thorium, is also naturally fissionable.

Fusion Processes

Energy may also be liberated by nuclear fusion. This is the principle of building up heavier atoms from lighter ones. The fission of a very heavy nucleus converts about 0.1% of its mass into energy. Larger fractions of the mass of very light nuclei may be converted into energy by their fusion into heavier nuclei so that fusion releases more energy than fission. As an example, four atoms of hydrogen may be changed into an atom of helium. This converts about 0.7% of the mass into energy, for the mass of four hydrogen atoms is 4.03252 and the mass of the helium atom is 4.00386. Other isotopes of hydrogen may also be used in the process. Deuterium (hydrogen with a weight of 2) and tritium (hydrogen with a weight of 3) combine to form an atom of helium and a neutron. This process converts about 0.4% of the mass into energy. Such a process of fusion is not an easy one. The atomic nuclei must be held together for an appreciable time. This can be accomplished only if the reactants are brought to a temperature of at least 100 million degrees centigrade. It has been found by experiment that this temperature can be reached by surrounding an ordinary atomic bomb with a mixture of deuterium and tritium. Thus an A-bomb is used to trigger an H-bomb.

Nuclear Weapons

The forces released by either process — fission or fusion — are tremendous. It would almost seem as if man could destroy himself with either the A-bomb or the H-bomb. Thus far we have witnessed only the destructiveness of the A-bomb. The first of these was detonated over Hiroshima August 6, 1945. As a result 78,150 were killed according to the best available reports and 36,425 injured. The number of those listed as officially missing was 13,983. Presumably most of these perished without trace. The destructive force of the bomb was felt over 27,000 acres. Most of the buildings in this area were destroyed.

Three days later, on August 9th, a second bomb was detonated over Nagasaki. This bomb killed 73,884 people and injured 76,796. No official list of the missing was published at Nagasaki, but it is estimated that the number of missing was about 8,000. Some 13,500 acres were devastated at Nagasaki. Because of the hilly terrain of the city, there was less destruction than at Hiroshima.

Yet these figures of death and destruction in these two cities do not tell the whole story. Since August 1945, 206,070 persons have been treated for various kinds of radiation sickness in the two cities. There are 6,572 people still detained in two bomb casualty clearance hospitals. Few of them are expected to live in the outside world again. At the beginning of June 1958, 45,835 survivors were still attending regular outpatient clinics. Between January 1 and August 15, 1958, there were 58 deaths in Hiroshima and Nagasaki listed as due to the aftereffects of the bombs that fell there.

Nor do even these figures tell the whole story. There are also effects on children born to survivors of the bombings. There are many reports of various types of injury to children born after the bombing. One report, which may be exaggerated, states that 70 per cent of the babies born to mothers who survived the blast are mentally retarded. Most of these were born with small heads and died before reaching puberty. It appears too that there has been a reduction in the number of male children born, the sort of reduction which would be expected if sex-linked lethal mutations had been induced.

Still another effect is to be seen in the increase of leukemia among the survivors of the blast. This has been showing up in individuals who were apparently uninjured or who have recovered from their injuries. As time goes on a number of these are developing leukemia. We would expect some leukemia in any population, but the incidence of leukemia is higher among the residents of Hiroshima and Nagasaki than we would expect.

Actually the full extent of the damage is still unknown and is likely to be unknown for centuries. Many of the mutations which have probably been induced are recessives. They appear only when the individual receives the gene for them from both his mother and father. Thus these will make their appearance only when two individuals carrying them marry. It will take many generations before the full extent of this damage can be estimated.

All of this is the result of the detonation of two medium-sized A-bombs. Today we have developed A-bombs that are much more powerful than the two which were used to bring about the surrender of Japan. In addition we have an even more awesome weapon in the H-bomb. It is thousands of times more powerful than the A-bomb and spreads its destruction over much larger areas.

Short-Range Nuclear Damage

In analyzing the potential damage from the A-bomb and the H-bomb we find that it is of several types. First there is the damage to the individual. The immediate damage consists of blast damage and of burns. This is no different from the damage done by conventional explosives such as TNT. At Hiroshima and Nagasaki a number of individuals were literally vaporized. Others were so badly burned that they could not be saved.

In addition many of the victims were found to have had reddened skin. Ulcers developed which healed slowly. The lining of the mouth, the stomach, and the intestines was also damaged. As a result of the damage to the digestive tract, the victims showed a considerable degree of nausea. Many of the victims lost their hair for a time. In some sterility developed as a result of damage to the reproductive cells. This latter damage, however, proved to be reversible, and many regained their ability to bear or beget children.

Damage to the circulatory system was particularly apparent in the two bombed cities. This proved to be a delayed type of damage. Some of the victims seemed to be making satisfactory progress until they were suddenly stricken with a blood disorder and succumbed. The red-cell-forming elements were injured, and as a result there was severe anemia. The blood platelets, responsible for the clotting of the blood, were similarly destroyed, and as a consequence multiple hemorrhages occurred in various parts of the body. Even the white cells were affected. These are the disease fighters of the body. They are produced in the same red bone marrow where the red cells are produced so that damage to the red cells would lead us to expect damage also to white cells. Here the great danger was an overwhelming bacterial invasion even though every effort was made to protect the individual from infection. It appears that the white cells are constantly combatting bacterial invaders of the mouth, nose, and throat. When the white cells were reduced in number, these bacteria quickly gained the upper hand, overwhelmed the individual, and brought about his death.

This was the immediate and short-range damage to the individual. But there were still other hazards. The same destructive force which damaged the red-and-white-cell-producing machinery may also cause changes in the bone marrow which lead to leukemia. In addition, it is likely that there will be an increase in bone cancer, in thyroid degeneration, in cataract of the eye, and a general shortening of the life span.

Studies at Hiroshima and Nagasaki indicated that the effect of radiation on embryos was particularly significant. Embryos grow much more rapidly than either children or adults. Hence they are especially susceptible to radiation damage. An exposure which brought only minor damage to the mother might easily result in the death of the embryo. The consequence was a great many miscarriages and stillbirths.

Long-Range Damage

Yet with all of this, the greatest damage is to future generations, the genetic damage which it is difficult to measure and assess. There are two extreme opinions on this topic, both of which are probably incorrect. The first of these is that all children born to parents who have been exposed to radiation will be abnormal monsters except for a few who will be supermen. The second opinion, equally wrong, is that there is no danger at all.

Statistics show that about 5 per cent of all children born in the United States have some clearly defined birth defect, such as epilepsy, mental abnormality, a structurally defective heart, defective liver, defective digestive tract, eye or ear defects, and the like. About three fifths of these defects are due to developmental abnormalities or birth injuries. These are instances in which something goes wrong in the process of embryonic development, or there is some injury in the birth process. Such defects are not hereditary and are of no long-range significance. About two fifths of the birth defects are of genetic origin. They are hereditary and are therefore of considerable concern. The damage may occur many generations before it shows up. A recessive character, as we have pointed out, will appear only when two parents who are carriers of the trait marry. Such a trait may be in the stock for many generations before it makes itself felt. It is for this reason that the full damage of the bombs dropped at Hiroshima and Nagasaki will probably not be known for at least 500 years. Only within that time is it reasonable to expect most of the defects to have appeared through marriage of carriers of recessive traits.

The inherited traits are the ones which are of considerable concern. The defects which they represent are permanent. They will be passed on to the children of those who have them. It is true that by modifying the environment we can counteract the effect of some of them. Diabetes, for example, seems to be an inherited trait. Yet the condition can be treated by the administration of insulin or of one of the newer oral drugs. Surgery may also be used to correct inherited defects. In this way many heart defects can be corrected. But how much better if they never occur! Moreover, there are some about which we can do very little. These include most of the mental deficiencies.

If we assume that 40 per cent of the defective children carry defects of genetic origin, this means that in the next generation, estimated to number about 200 million in the United States, we shall have to expect four million defective children whose defects are of genetic origin. This is the number we shall have to expect without any increase in radiation due to war, weapon testing, atomic power plants, and the like. These defects are brought about by background radiation, cosmic rays, naturally radioactive substances, chemical substances which cause mutation, and the like.

We know, for instance, that there are powerful rays reaching the earth from outer space constantly. These are called cosmic rays. They are believed to be high-energy protons. What their source is we do not know. Study of them is complicated by the fact that when the primary cosmic particles reach the earth's atmosphere they cause a disintegration of the air, producing a great variety of secondary particles such as electrons, protons, mesons, and very short gamma rays. These cosmic rays can and presumably do cause mutations which are responsible for some of the genetic defects present already at birth.

It is also apparent that people come into contact with naturally radioactive substances. Uranium and thorium ores disintegrate constantly, and the rays they give off can presumably cause mutations. There are also certain chemical substances which can cause mutations. These will add to the load of mutations and to the number of genetic defectives.

The damage that all these do is to the individual's reproductive cells. It is believed, for example, that a high-energy particle from a cosmic ray may strike a gene bringing about some sort of rearrangement in it. This rearrangement in the gene shows itself in the individual's offspring. The deviation from the normal gene is known as a mutation. Most mutations are harmful. They may be visibly harmful, or they may lower the individual's reproductive rate and in that way be harmful. Some geneticists believe that over 99 per cent of all mutations are harmful. Most mutations are also recessive, that is, they do not show themselves in the presence of the normal gene. Only when the individual has two recessive genes, one of which he has gotten from his father and one of which he has gotten from his mother, does the recessive characteristic appear.

It is not hard to understand why most mutations are harmful. Developmental processes are intricate, complicated, and delicately balanced. Ordinarily they proceed step by step from one stage to another. When a gene has mutated, a different path is followed, and consequently the development is different from the normal.

The genetic defects occurring in two per cent of all live births are presumably caused by natural forces over which we have no control. It is apparent that in some places the amount of radiation is greater than in others, and we would expect more defectives there. In areas where there is a great deal of uranium people are presumably exposed to greater radiation dangers. It would also seem reasonable to expect people living at higher altitudes to be exposed to greater danger from cosmic rays, since we know that the amount of radiation from this source increases with the altitude. Yet human beings have lived for many generations in parts of the world which have five times the background radiation normal to the United States. Whether their mutation rate is higher than that in the United States has not yet been established.

Radiation Damage

Our concern with radiation is with man-made radiation over which we presumably have control. This includes radiation from X rays, from fallout, from luminous wrist watches, and the like. It is this which has been studied in greatest detail. A few years ago a governmental Committee on the Genetic Effects of Radiation recommended that the average individual should be exposed to no more than 10 roentgens of artificial radiation up to age 30 and no more than 20 roentgens of artificial radiation up to age 40. Age 30 was used as one dividing point because by this time half the individual's children will have been born, and age 40 as the second dividing point because by this time most of the individual's children will have been born. The committee estimated that if this limit were maintained for the general population 50,000 defectives, in addition to those expected from causes over which we have no control, will be born in the next generation. Eventually the number of defectives from this amount of artificial radiation will total 500,000. This is the price which it is believed we shall have to pay for the use of artificial radiation. Studies reported at recent Congressional hearings tend to confirm the validity of these recommendations.

It should be noted that the chief source of artificial radiation today is X ray. It is estimated that the average individual receives from three to four roentgens from X ray in the first 30 years of his life. X ray is an important diagnostic tool. It is used to set broken bones and to treat cancer. A dentist uses X ray to find decay which otherwise might escape attention. Perhaps the most common form of X ray today is the chest X ray. This procedure has been widely sponsored by the various tuberculosis associations. It has been a means for locating many cases of otherwise undiagnosed tuberculosis. There is no question but that many cases have been located in the early stages when it was possible to cure them in a minimum period of time. Improvements have been made steadily in the technique, so that today the individual receives only about 0.2 roentgens from a chest X ray, and if it is properly directed only 0.005 roentgens reach the gonads. It is this latter quantity which is the most important. So far as mutations are concerned, only that radiation is of significance which reaches the gonads.

Because of the density of the tissue, dental X rays require more radiation. Usually about two roentgens are received from each dental X ray. However, very little of this radiation reaches the gonads; so that dental examinations are not important sources of radiation so far as mutations are concerned.

X rays are widely used in medical therapy. They are commonly used in the treatment of cancer to destroy malignancies. This is of little importance so far as genetic damage is concerned because most of the cancer patients who receive this therapy are in the postreproductive years. Other uses of X ray in therapy are of more importance. In some cases heavy doses of X ray — up to 300 roentgens — have been used in the treatment of sterility. Skin infections and skin eruptions of various sorts are treated with X ray. It is used, for instance, to treat acne, warts, and fungus infections.

The fluoroscope involves the same principle as the X ray and therefore involves a radiation hazard. It depends on the shadow produced on a fluorescent screen when objects are placed in the path of X rays. A fluoroscopic examination may require 100 times more radiation than is used in X ray.

It is only within recent years that we have recognized the hazards of radiation. First to be recognized were the possible cancer-causing effects of radiation. One of the early radiologists, who died only recently, had over 90 operations for cancer induced by excessive exposure to X ray. In more recent years we have become aware of the mutagenic properties of X ray and have realized that the amount of X ray should be reduced to a minimum. We must ask ourselves "Is this X ray necessary?" It appears advisable to reduce the number of chest X rays which are used for mass screening purposes. Mass tests for tuberculosis are still highly desirable and necessary. However, so far as the general public is concerned, it is probably advisable to conduct them by using tuberculin rather than X ray. The United States Public Health Service has recommended that the use of X rays for mass screening for tuberculosis be discontinued. Their use is still justified in areas and in circumstances where we may expect a large incidence of tuberculosis, in slum areas, prisons, and hospitals, for instance. X ray must also be used if the individual shows up positive on a tuberculin test. In this circumstance an X ray will show whether the tuberculosis is active or arrested. But because of the possible hazard, the use of X ray for mass screening of the general public does not seem to be justified, especially since another technique, the tuberculin test, is available.

The use of dental X rays seems to be justified. However, dentists should be aware of the possible hazards to themselves. They are likely to be exposed to much more radiation than any of their patients. Moreover, the number of dental X rays should be reduced to the number necessary for the determination of cavities.

There is no reason for discontinuing the use of X ray in cancer therapy. Here X ray is one of the few tools we have in treating this dread scourge. Moreover, most of the people who fall prey to this disorder are in the postreproductive years. Since their children have already been born, there is no danger of mutation.

On the other hand, X rays should be used only to a limited degree in the treatment of skin disorders and the like. There is a real hazard here, and the hazard should be weighed against potential good. There are some conditions in which X ray is the only possible therapeutic agent. But there are other cases in which other means are available and still others in which the amount of good accomplished is limited and hence does not justify the use of radiation.

It would seem that the use of X ray in treating sterility is particularly hazardous. The dosage used is very high. What must be considered is the possibility of bringing children into the world who are defective. This may well be an even greater cross than having no children at all.

One of the common uses of the fluoroscope is in the fitting of shoes. Shoe "X rays" are not X rays at all: they are fluoroscope pictures. Here the potential hazards do not justify the use of this tool, and in many states shoe X rays are illegal. There are other satisfactory methods of fitting shoes. Moreover, many of the machines in use are old and have little shielding. The result is that a great deal of radiation from the machine reaches the operator and the individual whose shoes are being fitted.

Still another source of radiation is the peacetime use of atomic energy. Those employed in atomic power plants, on atomic submarines, and in atomic research laboratories are likely to be exposed to some radiation in the course of their work. The suggested maximum amount of radiation for such workers has been 0.1 roentgen a day. Yet if an individual were exposed to that much radiation each day he would soon exceed the maximum permissible amount.

Shortening of life seems to be another effect of radiation. Animal studies have indicated that the life span of such an individual would be reduced by about three years even if he suffered no mutations which might be transmitted to his children. One study of human beings indicates that physicians who have little or no contact with radiation live an average of 65.7 years. Specialists who have some exposure to radiation — dermatologists, urologists, and the like — have an average life span of 63.3 years. Radiologists, however, have an average life span of only 60.5 years. Moreover, another study indicates that radiologists have a slightly lower proportion of normal children than other physicians. Because of the twin hazard of mutation and reduced life expectancy, the recommended maximum dosage has now been reduced to 0.03 roentgens a day. Workers are required to wear special radiation badges which are examined from time to time to determine the amount of radiation to which they have been exposed.

The Hazard of War

In addition to these hazards, there is, of course, the hazard of a nuclear war. By far the most serious problem in this case would be the number of deaths and the disruption of vital services. In all probability if nuclear weapons were used, hydrogen bombs rather than A-bombs would be employed. The force of the A-bomb is usually measured in kilotons, each kiloton being the equivalent of one thousand tons of TNT. The force of an H-bomb is measured in megatons, each megaton being the explosive power of a million tons of TNT. The H-bombs employed would probably have a force of about 10 megatons. Each bomb would dig a crater some 2,500 feet wide and some 240 feet deep. Everyone and everything within about 5,000 feet of the crater would be completely destroyed. In addition a majority of people within several miles of the explosion would be killed and buildings severely damaged. How far this zone of death would extend would depend to a large extent on the topography. Some would be killed outright by the blast and the heat; others would die as a result of the radiation which the bomb would give off. Anyone receiving more than 450 roentgens would die.

Beyond the zone of total death and destruction would be a zone of serious injury and much destruction. This would extend for several miles. Many people would be trapped by falling buildings. Some would be seriously injured by radiation. Those who were able to take shelter before the bomb exploded might be protected or might receive a minimum of injuries. However, this area would be radioactive. Rescue workers could not enter it until it was declared safe. Indeed it might well be that rescue workers would be unable to enter this area simply because of the magnitude of the problem which the bombing would cause.

Beyond this area of serious destruction there would be an area of some injury and destruction. This might extend anywhere from 75 to 90 miles. First-aid stations would be set up on the inner edges of this area. There would be a substantial number of injuries in this area. These victims, together with those able to walk or secure transportation from the area of serious destruction, would come to the first-aid stations for treatment. Here some decisions would have to be made as to who should receive first-aid treatment. It is generally assumed that the number of casualties would be too great to permit the treatment of all the injured. There simply will not be enough blood, plasma, antibiotics, and bandages to go around. Some will have to be favored over others in the casualty stations. The principles on which casualties in a mass disaster such as the detonation of a nuclear weapon are to be treated is known as triage. This has received considerable attention in the past years. It is agreed, for instance, that in the case of a nuclear disaster we shall not be able to afford the luxury of giving treatment to those who will probably die anyhow. The seriously injured will have to be screened, and if it appears that an individual cannot survive he will have to be passed up at the first-aid stations. Only a limited amount of help will be available to the aged. Further screening might have to be done on the basis of occupation and the contribution that the individual will make to the society that will survive the war.

Still another problem is the destruction of, and interference with, vital public services. As our society becomes more complex we become more dependent on these. Our grandparents were independent and self-sufficient; we are not. Consider what happens when the electricity is off for a time. Not only are we deprived of light but those of us who cook by electricity must be content with cold meals. Many of our homes are cold because our furnaces operate by electric controls. Men cannot shave because they use an electric shaver. Consider now what will happen if the electricity is off not only for a few hours but for days and even weeks. Add to this the likelihood that water supplies will be cut off. Natural gas lines will be disrupted. There will be no sewage disposal and no garbage collection. The burial of large numbers of dead will present a problem. Highways will be clogged by debris and jammed by those seeking to leave the disabled city. Men and women will be frantically seeking relatives.

There will also be danger to a much wider area than that affected by the initial blast. In some of the early tests a small town in Nevada 100 miles from the Yucca Flat testing ground received seven roentgens due to a freak shift of the wind. When the first H-bomb was detonated in the Pacific, a Japanese fishing boat, the *Lucky Dragon,* was 250 miles from the site. Yet a number of the men aboard suffered from severe radiation sickness, and there was one death. Months later tuna caught in these waters were dangerously radioactive.

It should also be noted that there are ways of increasing the amount of radioactivity from a bomb blast. A country on the verge of defeat might employ such methods. Or such methods might be employed if there were no plan to invade the country under attack. A jacket of cobalt around the bomb would be pulverized in the explosion and would shower radioactive cobalt over a wide area. This could make hundreds of square miles uninhabitable.

Recent Congressional hearings indicate that in case of a nuclear war we in the United States would have to be prepared for 50 million deaths. Twenty million serious injuries would have to be expected. Eleven and eight tenths million dwellings in the U. S. — more than a quarter of the total — would be destroyed, and 10 million others would be damaged. In addition there would be 13 million homes severely contaminated by radioactive fallout. About 50 per cent of the dwellings in the U. S. would have been destroyed or rendered unusable for a period of several months.

Fallout

What is the fallout problem, of which we hear so much? It is essentially this, that radioactive material from a bomb either dropped in actual warfare or tested in preparation for war gradually descends throughout the world, increasing the amount of radioactivity every individual is exposed to. A great deal of radioactive material is produced by either an A-bomb or an H-bomb. However, fortunately many of these particles have a short half life and are dangerous for only a very short time. The particles that cause considerable concern are those which remain radioactive for a much longer time. The particles from an A-bomb are found at about 40,000 feet. They are carried by the prevailing winds from west to east. About half of this material settles every 22 days. Most of these particles are short-lived and do not cause too much concern. Longer-lived particles, such as strontium-90, are of concern.

The problem of the debris from an H-bomb is more serious. These particles are found at about 100,000 feet. They settle much more slowly and are distributed over most of the earth. Some of these have a fairly long half life. Particularly dangerous is the radiation from strontium-90. There is also some danger from cesium-137 and from radioactive iodine. Strontium-90 has a half life of about 28 years. Cesium-137 has a half life of 33 years.

Let us examine the problem of strontium-90, which is probably the most dangerous of these fallout particles. It is the product of the detonation of a nuclear bomb. It is deposited in the stratosphere, then descends to the troposphere, and is widely distributed by the air currents. Gradually it falls over all the earth. It is incorporated into the protoplasm of plants. Some is absorbed by the roots, and some is absorbed directly by the leaves. The plant apparently absorbs strontium in proportion to its availability. It does not favor calcium over strontium. For a time it was thought that spreading lime on the soil would decrease the amount of strontium absorbed because the plant was thought to prefer calcium to strontium, but experimental evidence does not bear out this hope.

The strontium which has fallen is now available to grazing animals such as the cow. Some they may get from the surface of leaves which they eat; some has been incorporated into the plant itself. The strontium finds its way into the cow's milk. At this point there is a discrimination factor against strontium. It does not appear in the milk in proportion to its occurrence in the cow's diet. There seems to be a factor of between 7 and 10 against strontium in favor of calcium.

It appears that dairy products are the chief source of strontium-90 in man, though some strontium-90 also comes from the vegetables that we eat. The latter is minimal because of washing and removing the leaves. Humans also discriminate against strontium. Kulp reports a discrimination factor of 8 in man. Comar, Russell, and Wasserman report a factor of between 3 and 4. There is also a discrimination factor of about 2 across the placenta which tends to protect unborn children. In general it is believed that the differential factor may be as high as 25 for the newborn and not lower than 6 for adults, depending on the individual's food habits.

At the present time the amount of radiation received from fallout is from 0.001 to 0.005 roentgens a year. This is a very small amount. Yet it poses a real danger. The strontium and cesium are deposited in bones where it is likely that they will cause bone cancer and leukemia. Moreover, the danger from fallout is likely to continue for a long time. If the tests are continued, it is quite possible that we shall be receiving from 10 per cent to 40 per cent of the maximum permissible radiation dosage from fallout alone. To May 1959 it is estimated that 65 megatons (TNT equivalent) of fission energy had been injected into the stratosphere by all nuclear tests. If this is correct, this corresponds to about 100 pounds of strontium-90 in the entire stratosphere. It is believed that about 50 per cent of this strontium-90 has already fallen. A group of civilian scientists who act as advisers to the Atomic Energy Commission estimated in May of 1959 that the amount of total body external radiation resulting from fallout to date, together with future fallout from previous weapon tests, is less than 5 per cent as great as the average exposure to cosmic rays and other background radiation and less than 5 per cent of the estimated average radiation exposure of the American public to X rays for medical purposes. They also pointed out that human beings have lived for generations in parts of the world that have 100 times the average amount of radiation that the United States gets from fallout. They report that the amount of strontium-90 found in food and water is less of a hazard than the amount of radium normally present in drinking water used for decades in some parts of the United States. Others disagree with this interpretation; they feel the hazard is much more serious. At the present time fallout has tended to concentrate in the middle latitudes of the Northern Hemisphere, largely because of the 1958 bomb tests of the Soviet Union.

What Does It Mean?

Now what does all this mean for the Christian? Today he is surrounded by a welter of claims. Some people believe the hazards are really great; others minimize them. There are those who argue that we are poisoning the earth by weapon testing, and they plead for a permanent discontinuation of atomic testing. They argue that the United States should do this even if the Soviet Union refuses to agree to a discontinuation of atomic testing. Yet the Christian must recognize the right of the government to bear the sword. Indeed the government has an obligation to protect its citizens from the threats of aggressors. Certainly this includes not only the right to wage war but also the right to prepare for war by weapon testing.

At the same time there is no question but that weapon testing increases fallout, that fallout increases the dangers of bone cancer and leukemia. It also increases the chances of harmful mutations. It appears that the frequency of mutation is proportional to exposure, though there are some who believe that there is a minimum threshold which has to be reached before any mutations occur. The majority believe that the number of mutations in the general population is proportional to exposure. They stress the fact that all radiation is potentially harmful. It is as if there were a blindfolded rifleman on a 40-acre plot of ground firing at a man whose location he does not know. He is unlikely to hit him if he fires only once. Even this is possible though. But the more often he fires, the greater the likelihood that he will hit him. So it is with radiation. A small amount is unlikely to cause a mutation. But the greater the amount of radiation, the greater the chance that a mutation will occur.

For this reason weapon testing should be reduced as much as is consistent with national safety. There must be a real purpose to each test. As much data as possible should be gotten from each test. Tests should not be used merely to entertain and impress.

Moreover, the Christian should be active in the quest for peace. He must not only pray for peace; he must work actively for it. There can be no reckless rattling of the saber in the middle of the 20th century. Everything possible must be done to increase international understanding and to decrease international tensions. The day is probably gone when we could afford the luxury of sending an army after an errant citizen who had wandered into a danger zone. We shall have to reckon with the possibility of starting a nuclear war as we attempt to protect individual citizens. We shall have to weigh the consequences of various courses of action to see whether they may lead to a nuclear war.

PEACETIME USES
OF ATOMIC ENERGY

chapter

2

PEACETIME USES
OF ATOMIC ENERGY

In many ways the atom hangs like a sword of Damocles over our civilization. But as we have pointed out, the atom is itself not evil. It has tremendous potentialities for good, and God has intended that it should be used for good. Some of these potentialities for good have already been realized. Let us see what some of these are.

One of the most interesting developments has been the use of atomic processes to generate electricity. The importance of this development lies in the fact that it makes it possible for countries which have little or no coal, oil, or water power to enjoy the benefits of an advanced civilization. Many of the countries which are deficient in coal, oil, and natural gas do have large deposits of uranium and other radioactive minerals. It is hoped that these may be used to generate electricity and thus advance the industrialization of these countries.

At the present time most of the studies are being made in the United States, England, and the USSR. All of these have ample supplies of conventional fuels, although England's coal is of a low quality. Yet leaders of these countries feel they must experiment lest they be left behind by atomic developments. Moreover, only these countries have the resources necessary to carry on atomic experimentation.

At the present time there are six atomic power plants in operation in the United States. Four more are expected to be completed by the end of 1961. At that time capacity will jump from the present 400,000 kilowatts to more than 800,000 kilowatts. The first large atomic power plant was built at Shippingport, Pa., and supplies Pittsburgh with a part of its electricity. This plant is estimated to have cost about $110 million. It is not an economical operation at present. Electricity is produced at a cost of seven to eight mills a kilowatt hour in utility plants operating with conventional fuels. At Shippingport the comparable costs have been estimated at about 64 mills per kilowatt. At the present time the Shippingport plant is producing 60,000 kilowatts of power — a very small amount indeed.

The largest atomic plant presently in operation is the Commonwealth Edison's Dresden plant at Morris, Ill. It was completed in 1960 and is a boiling-water type reactor. It produces 180,000 kilowatts at a cost of 10 mills per kilowatt. If the expenses in connection with its construction which have been written off by the utilities and by General Electric Company are excluded, its cost of production is only seven and one half mills per kilowatt.

By 1965 it is predicted that there will be 20 atomic power plants in operation in the United States. These will produce about 2.6 million kilowatts. The largest plant so far proposed is the Hanford, Wash., plant. President Kennedy has proposed that it be erected by the federal government. It is to produce 760,000 kilowatts by 1964. When it is producing at maximum efficiency at some later date, it is believed it will produce electricity at between five and six mills per kilowatt.

So far there have been few problems in connection with nuclear power plants. Many have feared that something may go wrong and a nuclear explosion result. So far there has been no serious disaster, though three men lost their lives in an explosion near Idaho Falls in January 1961. The plants have generated electricity for months on end with only a few minor faults developing. Usually those parts that have failed have been conventional components which require the normal amount of maintenance. There have been very few defective fuel elements. The failure rate has been only three or four a year out of about 10,000 fuel elements. Reactors using metallic fuel usually achieve about 3,000 megawatt days per ton, so that one ton of uranium does the work of 10,000 tons of coal. Uranium oxide is used in some reactors. Its rate of burnup is about one third that of metallic uranium.

Newer types of power stations are on the drawing boards. These are expected to be much less expensive than the present power stations. A 500-megawatt station is scheduled to be completed in England in 1962. It is expected to produce electricity as cheaply as it is produced in coal-fired stations away from the coal fields. By 1982, it is believed, electricity generated in England by nuclear processes will cost only half as much as electricity generated by conventional processes. It is quite possible that progress will not be as rapid as these optimistic estimates would indicate. Recent studies have indicated that the cost of producing electricity by atomic processes has not decreased at the rate it was expected to decrease. Reports indicate that there is not so much enthusiasm for atomic power plants in England today as there was a few years ago.

At present the boiling-water reactor power station seems to be favored. These have a low system pressure, are small in size, and are comparatively simple. It is the cost of the station rather than the cost of the fuel, which makes nuclear power so expensive at present. The actual cost of the fuel is from 20 per cent to 40 per cent of the unit cost, depending on whether natural uranium or near natural uranium or a more highly enriched fuel is used. Fuel costs for graphite-moderated, gas-cooled reactors are estimated at about 2 mills per kilowatt. For heavy water reactors it is believed that the fuel costs can be brought down to 1 mill. It appears that nuclear fuel costs should in all cases be lower than conventional fuel costs.

Another thing to be considered in nuclear power stations is the load factor. High load factors are essential at present to counteract the present high capital costs. It appears that a nuclear power station could run continuously if there were no technical reason to prevent this. It is assumed that such a power plant will have at least a 75 per cent load factor, and it is on this basis that the 500-megawatt power station in Britain is expected to achieve parity with coal-fired stations in areas in Britain away from the coal fields.

It is probable that by the late 1960s, as the installed capacity of nuclear power stations grows, the available load factor will fall. By that time this is likely to be more than compensated for by further reduction of capital costs. Nuclear power costs in Britain, as we have indicated, are therefore expected to fall well below conventional costs by the late 1960s. The date of achieving cost parity with conventional electricity-generating processes will be later in such countries as the United States, where hydroelectric stations and stations using low cost coal or natural gas can generate power for only a few mills. In Italy it is believed that nuclear power at present would be about 10 per cent more costly than power from oil. In India it is believed that a 150-megawatt power station could achieve parity immediately. The actual date for achieving parity in most countries ranges from 1963 to 1973, depending on the circumstances of the individual country. The Organization for European Economic Co-operation predicts that western Europe will have an installed nuclear capacity of 10,000 megawatts by 1965. The United States has predicted that it will have 1,300 megawatts by 1963; the USSR 2,000 megawatts by the early 1960s. It is estimated therefore that the total capacity between 1965 and 1970 will be about 15,000 megawatts. It is generally agreed that by 1975 most new high-output power stations will be nuclear.

What about underdeveloped countries? In a country such as India the power requirements are doubling every six or seven years. As we indicated, it is believed that nuclear power stations would be competitive already today. India hopes to have an installed capacity of 500 megawatts by 1965. Japan is in a similar situation and hopes to have 750 megawatts by 1965. To a large extent the growth of nuclear power in other underdeveloped countries will depend on their indigenous fuel supplies, on the available loads, and on their state of technological development. It would be hard for nuclear power to compete with diesel power where power requirements are less than 30 megawatts and load factors are low. One of the problems in the underdeveloped countries is that technicians are even scarcer than scientists.

It appears that most reactors of the future will require an enriched fuel. It will be necessary to use uranium that has been processed to provide more U^{235} than is ordinarily present in uranium as it is mined. One way of providing this enriched fuel is through the use of plutonium from earlier reactors. Once started, the reactors could operate on natural or slightly enriched uranium by recycling the plutonium. Another plan involves the feeding of plutonium to reactors of a fast breeding type. This technique would result in a better use of the world uranium supplies. It appears, though, that uranium is so abundant that we shall not have to be especially conservation-minded regarding it. No doubt we shall want to develop these fast-breeding types of reactors, but there is no hurry for these. We can afford to spend a great deal of time in developing efficient ones. Fast reactors will probably not be in appreciable use before 1970.

It is also possible to use thorium as a fuel in a reactor. It has several advantages. However, a large investment of U^{235} or plutonium is required to start the thorium cycle. It is believed that thorium reactors will be coming into use by the late 1960s since large amounts of thorium will be available as a by-product of uranium mining.

It appears that radioactive materials are much more abundant than we once thought. Uranium appeared at one time to be a rather rare mineral. We know now that it is rather abundant. The agreement of the Atomic Energy Commission to purchase uranium at a fixed price made it attractive to seek out supplies of the mineral, and a great deal has been discovered. It appears that we can obtain at least 40,000 tons of uranium oxide a year at a cost of between $8 and $10 a pound. The ore reserves in South Africa, the United States, Canada, and France probably contain at least two million tons of uranium. On the basis of present geological data and the experience of the last 10 years we can expect to discover at least two million tons more. Present estimates are that we shall have available from two to four times as much uranium as we thought would be available to us as late as 1955. Assuming that the reserves behind the Iron Curtain in the USSR and in China are of the same order as in the Western world, it appears that the reserves of high grade ore are about 10 million tons of uranium. In addition there are almost limitless supplies of low-grade uranium ore in shales and phosphorites. Thorium is also relatively abundant. There are large reserves in India. These are likely to be a real blessing to that subcontinent. Canada also has large deposits. Recently a substantial amount was discovered at Blind River. This particular deposit contains one part of thorium to two parts of uranium oxide. World thorium reserves appear to be at least 500,000 tons.

What does this mean so far as energy sources are concerned? Once more God has not been niggardly in His gifts to man. He has provided us with an abundance of the raw material for this new source of energy. Assuming a 30 per cent burnup, which might be achieved by breeding, 10 million tons of uranium are the equivalent of 10,000,000,000,000 tons of coal. This is three times the world's estimated coal reserves. Moreover, before we run out of uranium we shall probably have developed fusion processes of generating electricity. As electricity generated by nuclear processes becomes more and more common we shall see a gradual disappearance of coal-fired electric power stations. Coal will be far too expensive and far too valuable to use it in generating electricity. Probably it will be used as a raw material for our synthetic chemical industry.

A European Atomic Energy Community, known as Euratom, has been set up in Belgium, France, West Germany, Italy, Luxembourg, and the Netherlands. It is planned to construct six large-scale nuclear power plants based on the type of reactors that have been developed in the United States. It is hoped to have about one million kilowatts of nuclear power available by 1963. Some of the participants have recently shown a lack of interest, and this target may not be reached. This should be sufficient to meet the power requirements of five million people in the Euratom area. The plants will be built, owned, and operated by utilities in the member states. The United States will sell Euratom enough U^{235} to cover the fueling and other requirements of the program over a 20-year operating period.

Several portable nuclear power plants have been developed. These are intended to provide electricity and space heat in remote areas. Such a portable plant would be particularly valuable for use at a remote military station. One such plant, developed in 1958, produced enough energy to generate 260 kilowatts of electricity and to provide 400 kilowatts of space heat. It is designed to operate for three years with each fuel loading.

In addition to the mineral reserves of nuclear materials, there is also a tremendous amount of raw material for nuclear reactions to be found in the oceans. It is estimated that a single bucketful of sea water holds a quantity of deuterium with the energy content of more than three tons of coal. The oceans contain *in toto* enough heavy water to supply us with energy, at the rate we are consuming it at present, for several billion years.

Someday thermonuclear energy will be converted directly into electricity. At present electricity is generated by indirect processes. In most cases the nuclear material is used to heat some agent such as water, which is then used to turn the turbines to generate electricity. This is a relatively inefficient process. A substantial portion of the energy is wasted in the process. It is likely that this difficulty will someday be overcome. This will eliminate heat transfer systems and bulky generators.

Fusion Processes

Fusion processes are also quite promising. For one thing, these are comparatively "clean." The "ash" from fusion is primarily helium, a harmless, inert gas. Fission, on the other hand, creates dangerous radioactive wastes. The Shippingport installation in one year of operation accumulates almost four times as much radioactive material as a very large A-bomb spews into the atmosphere. It is estimated that the quantity of strontium-90 produced by nuclear power plants will be so large by 2000 that roughly 16 million cubic miles of water will be needed to dilute it. This is more fresh water than there is in the world, including the polar icecaps. This is a problem which will have to be solved if we are to have a substantial amount of electricity produced by fission processes.

The problem with fusion is the same problem that we encounter in the H-bomb. Deuterium nuclei repel each other. Yet in fusion two nuclei of a light element such as deuterium must join together to release the energy. In the H-bomb this repulsion is overcome by tremendous heat. This is not feasible in the power plant. It is hoped that this repulsion can be overcome by the use of magnetic fields.

Atomic Ships

Atomic power has been used as a means of propulsion in several different types of ships. Probably the best known of these is the U. S. submarine *Nautilus*. Such an atomic submarine has more room because Diesel engines, fuel tanks, and batteries are not needed. Quarters are no longer cramped. Compared with other submarines they are actually luxurious. It was the *Nautilus* which attracted world-wide attention by traveling under the polar ice cap. A pressurized water reactor is used to develop steam for propulsion. It has proved to be remarkably reliable. When the *Nautilus* was finally refueled after sailing 60,000 nautical miles, it had consumed an amount of uranium smaller in size than an electric light bulb. A second U. S. atomic submarine has been named the *Seawolf*. It operates on a slightly different principle. Here liquid sodium extracts the heat from the atomic generator and transfers it to water. Steam is generated, and this steam spins turbines which drive the propellers.

Recently the Russians developed an atomic icebreaker, the *Lenin*. It has three pressurized water reactors which provide about 44,000 shaft horsepower for propulsion. It is believed that this atomic icebreaker will greatly aid the opening up of the 6,000-mile seaway north of Russia. The ship began its maiden voyage in September of 1959.

A combined passenger-cargo ship, the *N. S. Savannah,* is undergoing tests at present. The "N. S." stands for "nuclear ship." The ship has been named the *Savannah* in honor of the first American steamship to cross the Atlantic. This ship was commissioned in 1960. It has a pressurized water reactor developing 22,000 shaft horsepower. It is believed that the fuel costs are about equal to those of a similar ship propelled by fuel oil. However, capital costs are about three to four times higher than conventional capital costs. Before this type of passenger ship becomes commercially feasible, a drastic reduction of capital costs will be necessary.

The world's first nuclear powered cruiser, the *U. S. S. Long Beach,* has been constructed and underwent sea trials in July 1961. The United States expects to build a nuclear tanker with a boiling-water reactor for propulsion by 1962.

It is believed that this type of reactor will have lower capital costs than the pressurized water reactor. This should help bridge the cost gap. It is believed, though, that the cost of this tanker will probably still be above that of a conventional tanker.

Radioactive Isotopes

A great deal of work has been done with radioisotopes, artificially radioactive substances. The 92 naturally occurring elements have more than 900 radioactive forms. These can be used in a number of ways in medicine. They have been used, for instance, in the treatment of cancers which cannot be reached in any other way. They are introduced into the body, often by mouth. If the right isotope is chosen, it will localize itself in the tumor. Here it will give off various rays which will attack the tumor without harming the surrounding healthy tissue. Usually this treatment is effective in slowing down the cancer. Rarely is it possible to destroy the tumor completely with radioactive isotopes. Actually isotope therapy has not been too successful in cancer therapy because we have not always been able to localize the isotopes in the cancerous tissue.

Isotopes are also used to outline a malignant growth. This makes it possible to remove the growth surgically. The isotopes tend to be more abundant in the cancerous tissue than in the healthy tissue. It is possible to follow these with a counter and to outline the extent of the tumor.

Radioisotopes are also used in industry. They are used to examine castings and the like for flaws. They are used to control the thickness of paper. Several million meters of oil well bores have been logged by radioactive tracers. It is estimated that the use of radioisotopes in industry is already saving $400 million a year and that soon many billions of dollars will be saved by the use of the isotopes.

Russia reports that its savings through the use of radioisotopes are of a similar magnitude.

Radiocobalt and radiocesium will shortly be available in strengths on the order of 100,000 curies for industrial applications. These powerful radiation sources will be used to sterilize hospital dressings, pharmaceutical products, and other materials where chemical sterilization is less desirable. These radioisotopes can also be used to produce what are known as "grafted polymers." In these the properties of the original polymer are changed in such a way as to constitute an improvement. Thus a special styrene-polyethylene film has been produced which has much-improved properties for purifying brackish water. Other polymers of polyethylene and polystyrene have been developed which have a high strength and stability up to 250°C.

The movement of silt in river estuaries and harbors is now being studied with the help of radioactive tracers in many parts of the world. The pioneer work in this field was done in the Thames estuary. Labeled water is being used to trace the flow of water in rivers, sewers, and underground strata. This should prove important in the survey of water resources in underdeveloped areas and for the control of irrigation in arid areas.

A special polonium alpha-particle camera has been developed which makes it possible to measure small mass differences in microtome sections of biological material. Biochemistry too has been revolutionized by the availability of labeled components. It is possible to trace these through living plants and animals to see how they are metabolized. Most of the work has been done with carbon-14. Today tritium, hydrogen with an atomic weight of three, is being widely used. With its low-energy beta-emission, tritium allows very precise localization by autoradiographic techniques. This technique is already providing direct evidence on cell nuclear processes which formerly had to be inferred from indirect considerations.

Similar tracing processes are being employed in a study of the human being. Radioactive tracers are used in diagnosis and in the measurement of individual body functions. The void which once existed between what went into the body and what is excreted no longer exists. The researcher can trace intermediate metabolism by direct counting or by sampling tissues and body fluids. In recent years there has been increasing emphasis on shorter-lived radioactive tracers. These reduce the radiological dose to the subject. At the present time a million medical patients are being diagnosed or treated with radioactive isotopes each year. The chief medical use of these tracers is the location and treatment of tumors.

Over 90 per cent of the tire fabric and 80 per cent of the tin cans made in the United States are controlled in production by radioisotope thickness gauges. Industry also uses radioisotopes to locate leaks in oil pipelines and to measure the wear and corrosion of metals. Radiation is also used to vulcanize rubber and to start chemical reactions.

In agriculture, radiation has been used to develop rust-resistant oats and wheat. It has also been used to produce mutations of crops that give greater yields per acre and also to produce pest-resistant varieties. Early yield fruit has also been produced.

Gamma rays have been used by the Army Quartermaster Corps to destroy micro-organisms. In this way food can be preserved for weeks and months at room temperature. The food thus preserved has been eaten without any harmful effects. However, there have been some undesirable aftereffects. The Food and Drug Administration has not yet certified gamma-ray treated foods for market, and the

Quartermaster Corps has temporarily discontinued these studies.

Studies are also being carried on to determine the possibility of producing both power and radioisotopes from nuclear explosions. This would make both less expensive.

For every dollar of federal expenditure on peacetime uses of atomic energy, $750 is being returned to the national economy through the savings effected in industry, medicine, and agriculture. There is every reason to believe these savings will increase manyfold.

The Atom a Gift of God

Now what does all this mean for the Christian? He can only be thankful to God for this new source of energy. It promises new luxury and new ease. As our standard of living increases, we shall want more and more energy. Already the U. S. consumption of energy is about 160,000 kilocalories per person a day. This is 15 times greater than the energy required in a primitive agrarian economy and about nine times the world average. It is unlikely that conventional fuels can meet this need indefinitely. The atom, however, promises to be an almost unlimited source of energy. We have only scratched the surface. No doubt we shall become more and more efficient in releasing energy by fission processes. The whole area of energy from fusion remains to be explored. We have not even made a beginning here. God's bounty can be seen in the tremendous amounts of energy He has provided and His special goodness to our generation in the fact that we are permitted to begin to use this.

All of this also points up the problem treated in the earlier section, and that is the problem of seeing that this energy is used for good purposes. The difficulty is not in what we now have available; the difficulty is in the use of this energy. Will man use or abuse this gift of God? Here Christians must be the salt of the earth. They must see to it that these gifts of the Almighty are used for good and not for evil. They have a tremendous potential for good, and we must see to it that they are used in this way.

There is something else that must be kept in mind. That is that we as Christians must be sure we recognize God as the Source of these gifts. It is so easy to boast of one's own accomplishments, so easy to be proud of what our age has accomplished. Yet these are not things that we have earned. They have come to us from a bountiful heavenly Father. True, God gives daily bread indeed without our prayer, also to all the wicked. But we should pray God to lead us to know it and to receive our daily bread with thanksgiving. For only if we are thankful, and only if we show our thankfulness by using these gifts for good, will God continue to give them to us. If we bow down to these gifts and worship them instead of the Giver, God will take them away. It is very apparent that He can do this almost in the twinkling of an eye. We need only to have a nuclear war. Then all of the blessings we enjoy in our 20th-century civilization will disappear overnight. As we contemplate these wonderful gifts of God and as we look toward an even more wonderful future, our hearts must certainly be filled with gratitude to God for the blessing He has bestowed upon us in permitting us to spend our pilgrimage in the middle of the 20th century.

SATELLITES AND SPACE

chapter

3

SATELLITES AND SPACE

On October 4, 1957, the English language gained a new word. It was at 6:30 that night in New York that the monitor of a Russian news broadcast heard the startling announcement that the Russians had succeeded in launching an earth satellite. In this way the word *Sputnik* came into our language.

The launching of several artificial satellites was a part of the International Geophysical Year which extended from July 1, 1957, to December 31, 1958. By common international consent these 18 months, during which sunspot activity was to be at a maximum, were to be set aside for a study of various astronomical phenomena. One of the projects was an intensive study of the regions just beyond the earth's atmosphere. This was to be accomplished through the launching of several artificial satellites.

The first Sputnik was about 23 inches in diameter and weighed about 184 pounds. It had four metal rods, eight to nine feet long which served as antennae. These were folded back against the satellite when the carrier rocket was fired, but when Sputnik reached its orbit they swung outward on swivels.

Sputnik's speed was about 18,000 miles an hour, about five miles a second. The moon travels considerably slower: 2,400 miles an hour or two thirds of a mile a second. Sputnik had to travel faster because it was closer to the earth. Its orbit was elliptical. When farthest from the earth it was 583 miles above the earth's surface. When closest to the earth it was 143 miles above the earth's surface. The moon itself is about 225,000 miles from the earth. The closer to the earth an object is, the greater the earth's gravitational attraction for it. The speed with which the object moves forward must be great enough to keep it from falling to the earth and yet not great enough to escape the earth's gravitational pull entirely. Sputnik's carrier, which was not so far out in space, had to move faster than Sputnik itself in order to keep from falling to earth. The moon travels around the earth in about 27 days and eight hours. Sputnik made the trip in about 96 minutes.

Aboard Sputnik were two chemical batteries, two radios, and internal temperature and pressure gauges. The radio transmitters were responsible for the familiar "beep" of Sputnik. The power with which these transmitted was about one watt — enough for ham radio signals to be transmitted from the United States to Australia. We do not know what information, if any, the transmitters relayed. It may be that they broadcast information on temperature and pressure in a code intelligible only to the Soviets. Others believe no information at all was transmitted. Sputnik was filled with nitrogen, presumably to help get rid of the heat developed by the electronic equipment.

Sputnik remained in orbit from October 4, 1957, to January 4, 1958. In this time it made 1,370 revolutions. Its contact with the atmosphere gradually slowed it down until the gravitational pull of the earth finally pulled it into the thicker atmosphere close to the earth where it quickly slowed down and then burned up in the earth's atmosphere. The first Sputnik was also known as 1957 Alpha.

Sputnik II

On November 3, 1957, a second Soviet satellite was launched. Scientifically it was known as 1957 Beta. Popularly it was known as Muttnik. It was much larger than Sputnik I, weighing 1,100 pounds. In shape it was a stubby cylinder.

It was the size of these two Sputniks that excited the amazement and admiration of American scientists. The essential problem of launching a satellite is that of developing enough thrust to put the satellite into orbit. Three rockets were used to put Sputnik I in orbit. These would have had to develop a thrust of 200,000 pounds, much more than American rockets could develop.

Sputnik II contained chemical batteries, two radios, and equipment to measure temperature, pressure, ultraviolet rays, X rays, and cosmic rays. In addition there was a dog named Laika aboard which was kept alive for several days in an air-conditioned cylinder. Here instruments measured its pulse, respiration, and blood pressure.

Sputnik II continued aloft until April 13, 1958. At its farthest point from the earth it was 1,000 miles away. Its closest approach was 132 miles. In addition to information on temperature and pressure it is believed that the satellite relayed information on the adjustment to weightlessness which the dog passenger made.

American Satellites

The first satellite to be orbited in 1958 was an American satellite. It was the Army's Explorer I and was sent into orbit January 31, 1958. Because it was the first 1958 satellite, it is known as 1958 Alpha. Explorer I was a small cylinder, 6×80 inches in diameter. It weighed almost 31 pounds. Thus it was only about one sixth the weight of Sputnik I. At its farthest point from the earth Explorer I is 1,573 miles away; at its closest approach it is 224 miles away.

Explorer I spins at about 700 revolutions a minute. It contains two mercury batteries and two radios. In addition there is equipment for measuring temperature, density of the air, cosmic ray intensity, and the impact of small micrometeors. The satellite is equipped with four whiplike antennae.

Explorer I indicated temperature ranges from 32°F to 104°F. It also revealed a belt of high intensity radiation about 600 miles from the earth. Explorer I is still aloft. It is expected to remain in orbit for three to five years.

The second satellite to be orbited in 1958 was also an American one. It was sent into orbit by the Navy. Because it was the second of the year it is known as 1958 Beta. It is also known as Vanguard I. It was orbited March 17, 1958. Vanguard I is even smaller than Explorer I. It is a 6.4 inch sphere weighing about 3.3 pounds. The launching vehicle was a Vanguard rocket 72 feet long with a 4-foot base. Its orbit ranges from 2,465 to 404 miles above the earth. One of the remarkable things about Vanguard I is that it contains six solar batteries as a power source for one of its radios. These depend on the energy of the sun. It is believed that these will last almost indefinitely so that this satellite will continue to broadcast information as long as it remains aloft. A second radio was operated with conventional mercury batteries. This transmitter went dead after two weeks.

The average temperature inside the satellite appears to be about 40°F. Temperature is measured by determining the shift in the radio frequencies. Vanguard I is still aloft and is expected to remain aloft for about 200 years.

On March 26, 1958, an Army satellite was again successfully launched. This was known as 1958 Gamma, Explorer III. The launching vehicle was identical with that used to launch Explorer I — a four-stage rocket with one liquid fuel stage and three solid fuel stages. Explorer III was a cylinder, 6×80 inches. It weighed 31 pounds. Its orbit varied from 1,741 miles above the earth to 118 miles above the earth. Like Explorer I it had two mercury batteries and two radios and instruments for measuring temperature, density of the air, cosmic ray intensity, and impact of micrometeors. In addition it had a tape recorder which collected data for the entire orbit. The tape moved about four feet during each revolution of the satellite. It played back the information it had gathered in about five seconds.

The batteries on Explorer III lasted for two months. The information relayed back from this satellite confirmed the existence of a deadly belt of radiation some 600 miles from the earth's surface. Temperature measurements within the satellite indicated that it would be possible for men to survive in the areas of space covered by the satellite. The atmosphere was much more dense than expected: about 10 times as dense as was expected at 150 miles. Further studies have indicated that there may be a thin atmosphere extending as far as the sun. It may be that nowhere between the earth and the sun is there the vacuum that was once thought to exist. Studies of the impact of micrometeors indicated that this might not be as serious a problem in space travel as was originally thought. This finding was important since it was thought that micrometeors, tiny bits of matter whirling around in space, might constitute a real barrier in space travel. It was feared that large numbers of these might strike a space vehicle with the speed of bullets and might make space travel impossible. Evidence from Explorer III does not indicate that this will be a major problem of space travel. Explorer III fell in mid-1958.

Sputnik III

The fourth satellite to be sent aloft in 1958 was a Soviet satellite, Sputnik III, or 1958 Delta. This was sent into orbit May 15, 1958. It was a very large cone-shaped satellite. It weighed 2,925 pounds and was 11 feet 9 inches in height with a 5-foot 7-inch base. According to the Russian reports, Sputnik III contained over a ton of instruments. These included chemical and solar batteries, a magnetron, photomultipliers to study the sun's radiation, apparatus to register cosmic ray photons, magnetic ionized manometers, ionic traps, an electrostatic flux meter, mass spectrometer tubes, apparatus to register the intensity of cosmic rays, and the impact of micrometeors.

Sputnik III traveled from 1,181 to 143 miles above the earth. The final rocket which fired it also went into orbit and was visible to the naked eye. What data has been gained from this huge satellite is not known. First reports regarding micrometeors were in disagreement with the information gathered from Explorer III. The Soviet satellite reported a great many more collisions with micrometeors. However, later reports tended to agree with the American findings that the danger from micrometeors to space travel is not as great as was previously thought. This satellite, too, has fallen.

Other American Satellites

On July 26, 1958, another American satellite was orbited. It was another Army satellite known as Explorer IV,
and because of the time of its launching it was known as
1958 Epsilon. It was launched by the same type rocket as
was used to launch Explorer I and II. Like the other
Explorers it too was a cylinder but was slightly heavier,
weighing about 38.4 pounds. It traveled between 1,380
miles and 157 miles above the earth. The chief purpose of
this satellite was to measure cosmic rays. It was equipped
with two radios, both battery operated. In addition it had
two Geiger-Mueller counters and two scintillation counters
on faces of photocells. These latter can be used to measure
several levels of radiation. It fell in October 1959.

Evidence gained from Explorer IV indicates that radiation doubles for each 60-mile altitude above 250 miles up
to the farthest point from the earth measured by the satellite. At 1,200 miles the dosage is about 10 roentgens an
hour. This poses a real problem, since the maximum recommended human dosage is about that quantity in 30 years.

On October 11, 1958, a Pioneer rocket was sent aloft.
This was a rocket, not a satellite. It was hoped that this
rocket would reach the moon. The launching vehicle was
88 feet long and weighed 52 tons. The rocket was fired
vertically, but it wandered about 3½° from its intended
path. As a consequence it did not reach the moon but disintegrated after about 43 hours. It reached a velocity of
23,500 miles an hour. This was only 1,500 miles an hour
less than the speed necessary to escape the earth's gravitational pull.

The rocket carried batteries, an ion chamber to measure
radiation, an electronic scanner, and telemeters for determining meteorite density and the magnetic fields of the
earth and the moon. In addition it carried a TV infrared

camera to "see" the other side of the moon if it went into orbit.

Because of the reduced gravitational pull of the earth, the weight of the Pioneer at 79,000 miles, the maximum distance which it reached, was only 1/400 of its weight at the surface of the earth. For that reason it "floated" at about that altitude for two hours before falling back to the earth. Reports transmitted from the rocket indicate that radiation decreased from four roentgens an hour at 5,000 miles to two roentgens an hour at 17,000 miles.

One interesting thing in connection with Pioneer I was that tracking station operators in England and Hawaii were able to talk to one another by bouncing radio waves from the rocket.

On December 6, 1958, another Pioneer rocket was fired from Cape Canaveral, Fla. It had been hoped that it would reach the moon, but it was unsuccessful in this respect. After a flight of 38 hours and 6 minutes it re-entered the atmosphere and disintegrated. This rocket was known as Pioneer III. Pioneer III provided information on temperature and on the radiation zone. Throughout the probe the temperature inside the rocket remained at about 100°F. The information on the energy level and on the extent of the radiation belts was also of importance.

The Russian Mechta

The year 1959 began with a dramatic Soviet achievement. On January 2 a Soviet rocket known as Mechta ("Dream") blasted off. It carried 800 pounds of instruments. Within a few minutes it had attained its blast-off speed of more than 25,000 miles an hour — enough to escape the earth's gravitational pull. It came within 4,700 miles of the moon on Jan. 4 and then went on to become an artificial planet of the sun on Jan. 7. There are some who believe that it was originally intended as a moon rocket but that through a slight miscalculation it missed the moon and became a planet of the sun. The Soviets have insisted that it was their original intention to make it a tenth planet.

The total bulk of Mechta, also known as Lunik I, was a ton and a half. It was essentially the last stage of a multi-stage space rocket. Sixty-two hours after launching the Soviets lost contact with their rocket. Mechta continued to move away into space. It is believed that eventually it will assume a 15-month elliptical orbit around the sun. It will vary from 91 million miles to 122.5 million miles from the sun. The instruments and power source, together with the container, weighed 794 pounds. Two radio transmitters were aboard which went dead when the rocket was 373,125 miles from the earth. In addition Mechta carried special equipment designed to produce an artificial comet in the form of a sodium cloud. This was formed Jan. 3 and was visible for several minutes in the constellation Virgo.

Since Mechta has no atmosphere there is nothing to cause erosion or corrosion on the artificial planet. It will therefore lead a stressless and strainless existence. Once it gets into orbit, its physical system will be in a perfect equilibrium. It is for this reason that there is little likelihood of its being pulled into the sun or drifting off to some remote part of the solar system. Meteors are probably the greatest hazard to its longevity, but there is little chance that it will run into a meteor large enough to hurt it. No doubt it will collide with tiny meteorites, but these will probably do no more than nick its surface slightly.

It is believed that Mechta's surface was treated to protect it from the destructive effects of temperature extremes. But even if rapid fluctuations of intense heat and cold were to crack and pulverize it, it would continue to orbit as a unit. Out in space there is no force to pull anything apart.

The earth itself may pose a slight problem to Mechta. At its closest approach to the sun it may frequently intersect the earth's orbit. It will come into the vicinity of the earth itself once every five years. Yet even then it will be millions of miles away. Only through some freak occurrence will it be deflected from its orbit. The likelihood is that it will continue to orbit indefinitely.

At the present time Mechta is invisible even to the most powerful telescope. When it does approach the earth's vicinity again a powerful telescope might with some luck pick it up. It is tumbling as it travels, and this should give it an identifying twinkle.

It is probably not correct to call Mechta another planet. It is too small. Nor is it the only body in addition to the planets revolving around the sun. In all likelihood there are thousands of asteroids of a similar size in orbit around the sun.

Vanguard II

On February 17, 1959, a second Vanguard satellite was orbited. It is believed that it may remain in orbit indefinitely. It travels from 2,050 miles to 335 miles from the earth. Vanguard II weighs 21½ pounds and circles the earth every 126 minutes. It does not have the solar batteries of Vanguard I; it is equipped only with conventional batteries.

This satellite is intended to gain information about our weather. When it is closest to the earth, its photocells see only a relatively small strip. At its farthest point from the earth, they see a band almost seven times as wide. As the satellite spins and moves forward on its orbit, successive strips are traced out. These are reflected from a mirror onto an infrared photocell which produces an electrical response or fluctuation depending on the light intensity received. In this way the electronic eye differentiates clouds, water, and land masses.

A tiny tape recorder stores this information on magnetic tape. About 75 feet are required to store almost 60 minutes of data. A radio is triggered by impulse from the earth which causes the transmitter to broadcast to the earth in less than 60 seconds what was picked up in the previous hour. These transmitted data are recorded on a magnetic tape and analyzed by an electronic brain. The processed information is turned out in a series of crude strip photographs which are fitted together like aerial photographs. The result is a long chart of cloud conditions which Vanguard II has seen in a quick trip over the sunlit portions of the earth.

Undoubtedly Vanguard II is only a crude forerunner of reconnaissance devices, but it is already important because its crude observations may enable scientists to observe changes in the earth's cloud cover. If advancing and stationary storm fronts can be discerned quickly, then weather experts will be able to predict coming weather patterns quickly and accurately. This would be of supreme importance in the case of hurricanes and typhoons. These superstorms show marked cloud patterns easy to discern. They have been noted on high altitude rocket photographs. If their wind directions and paths could be forecast, many lives and injuries would be saved. In addition there would be a saving of millions of dollars of potential damage. Probably such forecasting would require more than one weather eye Vanguard since the weather forecasters would need sequences of mosaic pictures separated by a few hours. Clearer sets of pictures would also be highly desirable. These would be possible if a high-resolution TV camera were used.

The real significance of Vanguard II is that for the first time it gave scientists a platform on which to stand out in space and look back at the earth. True, it is a very crude platform, but in any case it represents real progress. Future reconnaissance satellites may well traverse the globe, watching everything that goes on and faithfully reporting it.

Pioneer IV

On March 3, 1959, the United States succeeded in launching an artificial asteroid. Like the other Pioneer rockets it was launched from Cape Canaveral, Fla. Pioneer IV, as it is known, contained a cone-shaped package of instruments. The capsule weighed 13.4 pounds. It was therefore much lighter than the Russian Mechta. Pioneer IV was tracked for 90 hours by a number of stations located in various places on earth. At that time its batteries ran out. At one stage there were three stations tracking it at once. The artificial asteroid was gold plated to eliminate the need for radio antennae. Gold itself is an excellent conductor of radio waves. The radio transmitter itself was about the size of a cigarette and weighed as much as a five-cent piece. Tracking stations reported that its signals were clear to the end.

It is believed that Pioneer will travel around the sun once every 392 days. This is longer than the earth takes to make the same trip, but a shorter time than Mechta. Like Mechta it is believed that Pioneer IV will remain in orbit indefinitely.

Pioneer IV carried two tiny Geiger counters to measure the intense radiation in some parts of space. The information radioed back has been of considerable help in determining and outlining the belts of radiation through which a potential space voyager must travel.

Discoverer I

A few days earlier, February 28, a satellite known as Discoverer I was launched by the U. S. Air Force from Vandenberg Air Force Base in California. This was the first attempt to put a satellite into polar orbit. Such a launching is impossible from Cape Canaveral because the satellite would have to travel over inhabited areas which it might damage severely if it failed to go into orbit. Discoverer I was intended to make possible a study of that part of the earth's surface that could not be studied by previous satellites. It was also intended to test the theory that there is a gap in the radiation belts at the North and South poles. It is believed that the poles may deflect the charged particles that make up the Van Allen layers and thus provide a radiation-free path into outer space. The satellite also passed over the Soviet Union. It contained 40 pounds of instruments. The launching was not too successful. For a time only weak signals were heard. Occasionally a signal was heard after hours of silence. Only five days after the launching did the announcement come that the satellite was in orbit. However, it was not spotted visually. Possibly the reason for this is that it passed over inhabited sections of the earth only in bright daylight or in darkness. The Air Force has suggested that the fault was not in the launching equipment but in the instrumentation of the payload. One theory is that the transmitter worked only feebly or intermittently. Another is that the satellite's stabilizing system failed, allowing the satellite to tumble over and over. This might have made its directional signals hard to receive on earth. It remained in orbit for only a few days.

Lunik II

In September 1959 the Russians succeeded in hitting the moon. This dramatic achievement coincided with the visit of Premier Khrushchev to the United States. The vehicle was called Lunik II and consisted of a sphere weighing 859.8 pounds. The sphere was carefully sterilized to avoid contaminating the surface of the moon. Lunik II contained cosmic ray counters, three radio transmitters, and a magnetometer to measure the moon's magnetic field. Lunik II was traced on its historic flight by the beeps which emanated from its radio transmitter. It was tracked not only in the USSR but also by the Jodrell Bank radio telescope in England. It struck the moon about 12:05 A. M. on September 13, 1959. At that time the beeps suddenly ceased. The point of impact seems to have been at or near the Sea of Serenity, which looks like the left eye of the man in the moon. It is possible that the last stage of the rocket which propelled Lunik II also landed on the moon.

It appears from information relayed back by Lunik II that the moon has no magnetic field. As a consequence of this there is no Van Allen radiation layer circling the moon.

Shortly after Lunik II the United States fired a third Vanguard satellite. It was a tapered tube 26 inches long and weighing about 100 pounds. Vanguard III contains a magnetometer which, it is hoped, will permit mapping of the magnetic field that surrounds the earth. The satellite also contains chambers sensitive to the X rays given off by the sun during solar flares.

Lunik III

Lunik III was launched by the Russians at 5 A. M. October 4, 1959. It went from the earth to the moon and then returned to circle the earth as an artificial satellite. Its importance lies in the fact that it is the first artificial satellite to orbit the moon. With it photographs of the back side of the moon were made, that section of the moon's surface which never faces the earth and which consequently

72

has never been seen. These pictures show that the other side of the moon is rather monotonous so far as general features are concerned. The more prominent features have been named by Russian astronomers. Lunik III entered the earth's atmosphere early in March of 1960 and burned up.

On October 13, 1959, the United States launched a seventh Explorer satellite. This satellite weighed about 91½ pounds. Explorer VII looked something like a gyroscope. It is expected to remain aloft for 20 years. It contains instruments to measure cosmic rays in and below the radiation belt, density of micrometeorites, and ultraviolet radiation from the sun. The satellite's batteries are charged by solar cells. One cell has been left unprotected from cosmic radiation and micrometeorites. If it continues to operate, it may be possible to eliminate some protective devices from space ships. This will result in a saving of weight.

Pioneer V

On March 11, 1960, the United States launched a 94.8 pound aluminum satellite from Cape Canaveral. This was known as Pioneer V. The satellite was 26 inches in diameter and went into orbit between the earth and Venus — inside the orbit of the earth. In this respect it differed from both Pioneer IV and Lunik I, both of which travel between the earth and Mars. The satellite has some 4,800 silicon cells in four paddles. It is to take 311 days to complete its circuit of the sun. Two transmitters are aboard, a 5-watt transmitter and a 150-watt transmitter. The transmitters are silent until they are activated by one of three ground stations. Contact with the satellite was maintained for about five months. After that time the satellite had traveled too far in space. It is hoped that it will be possible to re-establish contact in 1963 when the satellite comes within 50 million miles of the earth if the instruments hold up under the stresses of a space environment.

One of the chief purposes of Pioneer V is to provide a more accurate method of measuring astronomical distances. It will provide this more accurate yardstick by measuring more exactly the distance between the earth and the sun. In addition the satellite carries instruments for measuring high energy radiation such as we receive from the sun. It also has instruments for counting micrometeors and for measuring the strength and direction of magnetic fields in space.

Tiros I

A television and infrared observation satellite, Tiros I, was launched by the United States from Cape Canaveral on April 1, 1960. The 270-pound satellite was planned to go into a circular orbit 400 nautical miles above the earth's surface. So successful was the launching that its actual orbit is 378.7 miles at perigee and 407.2 miles at apogee. Its orbital time is 99:15 minutes.

The primary purpose of Tiros I was to send back pictures of cloud cover. It has two television cameras which can take pictures every 30 seconds for 32 exposures. The 500-line pictures will be stored on magnetic tape and read off on demand from ground contact stations. Power is supplied by nickel-cadmium batteries which are charged by solar cells. One camera covers a small area within the range of the larger camera. The clock timer in the narrow angle camera failed shortly after launching so that pictures from this camera were available only on direct command. While Tiros I will remain in orbit for many years, it transmitted pictures for only a few months.

Transit I-B

On April 13, 1960, a navigational satellite, Transit I-B, was launched by the United States. It was intended to explore the possibility of providing a reliable means of fixing the positions of surface craft, submarines, and airplanes. By 1963 four navigational satellites are expected to be traveling in evenly spaced orbits. By tuning in with special receivers ships will be able to determine their precise positions.

Discoverer XI

An 11th Discoverer satellite was launched on April 15, 1960, from Vandenberg Air Force Base. It carried a 300-pound capsule intended to be ejected and retrieved. The capsule was properly ejected, but because of the malfunctioning of devices intended to slow it down it went into orbit instead of entering the earth's atmosphere. It fell April 26, 1960.

Missile Warning Satellite

On May 24, 1960, a 5,000-pound missile warning satellite, named Midas II, was placed into orbit by the Air Force. The Midas satellite circles the earth every 94 minutes at a distance of 300 miles. The satellite is intended to detect heat radiation from the exhaust flames of a missile rocket engine. It is not expected that the Midas satellite will be a reliable device until 1963. Midas II will remain in orbit for about three years. Shortly after launching something went wrong with the system of radioing orders so that it was not possible to test the detection devices during actual missile launchings. Another Midas was launched July 12, 1961.

The Russian Space Satellite

On May 15, 1960, the USSR launched a 9,988-pound satellite, Sputnik IV, into a nearly circular orbit around the earth. The satellite contained a pressurized cabin containing a dummy human figure and equipment for a future manned space flight. On command the 5,510-pound cabin was to separate for descent to the earth. According to the Russians, no attempt was to be made to retrieve the cabin. It was intended to burn up in the denser layers of the earth's atmosphere. There were those who suggested that the cabin actually contained a human astronaut but that the Russians were guarding against the failure of their experiment by announcing that it did not. It is generally believed that the cabin was supposed to return to earth, but that a malfunction caused it to go into orbit.

The satellite circles the earth every 91 minutes. Radio signals are being sent out from it. It is easily visible, being of the second magnitude in brightness or approximately the brightness of one of the Big Dipper stars. It is still in orbit and has been in orbit longer than any Russian satellite.

A Piggyback Satellite

On June 22, 1960, the United States scored a space "first" by launching a piggyback satellite. A 42-pound radiation satellite was launched with a 232-pound navigational satellite. Only after they were in orbit did the two separate. The radiation satellite, 20 inches across, is designed to measure radiation in the ionosphere. The larger satellite, 36 inches in diameter, has been named Transit II-A. Like Transit I-B it is intended to make possible a more accurate fixing of position by ships at sea, submarines, and the like.

Recovering Capsules from Space

On August 10, 1960, Discoverer XIII carrying a 300-pound instrument capsule was launched in a polar orbit. Two hundred miles over the North Pole the capsule was released and began its re-entry into the earth's atmosphere. The capsule was finally recovered from the Pacific Ocean 330 miles northwest of Honolulu and hauled aboard a Navy helicopter. This marked the first time a man-made object had been recovered from orbit.

Eight days later Discover XIV was launched. This time the capsule was recovered in the air as it floated earthward.

The Echo Satellite

On August 12, 1960, a balloon satellite, Echo I, was launched by the National Aeronautics and Space Administration. The aluminum coated plastic balloon was folded in a 28-inch container. When inflated it was 100 feet in diameter. Echo I is easily seen, circling the earth every 121 minutes. It was used to reflect a message recorded by President Eisenhower between stations in Goldstone, Calif., and Holmdel, N. J.

Russian Space Triumphs

On August 19, 1960, the Russians orbited Sputnik V. The satellite had a weight of about five tons. Attached to it was a cabin. This was released August 20 from an altitude of 198 miles and landed within six miles of the calculated landing site. Aboard the cabin were two dogs, Belka and Strelka, 13 white mice, 15 gray mice, two white rats, fruitflies, several plants, seeds, bacteria, and a small segment of human skin.

A sixth Sputnik was launched December 1, 1960, and a seventh Sputnik on February 4, 1961. There were several reports of heartbeats supposedly heard from Sputnik VII.

On February 12, 1961, Sputnik VIII was launched. This satellite in turn was used to send another satellite winging into space toward Venus. The Venus probe weighed 1,419 pounds. It was intended to intercept Venus toward the end of May 1961. Radio contact with the Venus probe was lost in March 1961. It was not possible to determine whether the probe reached its goal.

On March 9, 1961, Sputnik IX was launched. Weighing five tons, it carried a dog named Chernushka (Blackie). Once more the cabin was released, and the dog was recovered. On March 25, 1961, Sputnik X was launched. It carried a dog named Zvezdochka (Little Star) and other small animals.

American Advances in Space

Late 1960 and early 1961 also saw some American space triumphs. On October 4, 1960, a Courier I-B satellite was launched by the Army from Cape Canaveral, Fla. The Courier was essentially a communications satellite. Initially it transmitted a message from President Eisenhower to Secretary of State Herter at the United Nations. The Courier was able both to send and to receive messages. In a five-minute period 372,500 words can be received by satellites of this type. These may then be stored on a tape recorder and on command transmitted back to earth when the vehicle is over another station.

On November 3, 1960, Explorer VIII was launched in an elliptical orbit. Its purpose was to investigate the ionosphere. Discoverer XVII was launched in a polar orbit on November 12. It was a part of the American intelligence program and of the missile early-warning system. Its capsule was caught by an Air Force plane over the Pacific.

On November 23 Tiros II was launched. This 280-pound drum-shaped satellite has 9,260 solar cells. Its orbit is a nearly circular one 400 miles above the earth's surface. The satellite is equipped with two cameras, one a wide angle camera intended to cover 750 miles, the other a narrow angle camera intended to cover 75 miles. The latter was planned to show cloud formations in fine detail. It was believed it would be able to photograph individual thunder clouds. Tiros is also equipped with five infrared detectors. The wide angle camera did not operate properly, but the narrow angle camera proved to be satisfactory. A third Tiros, intended chiefly as a hurricane hunter, was launched July 12, 1961.

On December 7 Discoverer XVIII was launched in polar orbit. A 300-pound satellite, it, too, discharged its capsule, which contained bone marrow, blood cells, and tissue from the underside of the human eyelid. It also contained fungus spores and algae. The capsule was designed to study the effects of radiation on living tissue, particularly human tissue. The capsule was caught by an Air Force C-119 cargo plane. Discoverer XX, launched February 17, 1961, from Vandenberg Air Force Base in California, weighed 2,450 pounds.

A second Samos satellite was launched in polar orbit from Point Arguello, Calif., on January 31, 1961. This, too, was a part of a missile early-warning system.

On February 16 Explorer IX was launched from Wallops Island, Va. This was orbited with a solid fuel Scout rocket. It consisted of a 12-foot coated aluminum balloon with heat reflecting white spots. Because of this it was known as the "polka dot satellite." Its purpose was to measure atmospheric density.

Two days later Discoverer XXI was launched in a polar orbit. Its significance was that its engines were restarted on signal from the ground. This indicated the feasibility of maneuvering a space craft from the ground.

On March 25 a 78-pound Explorer X was launched in a highly irregular orbit. It traveled in an orbit from 94 miles to 120,000 miles above the earth. The instruments aboard were intended to study the protons shot out from the sun and to measure magnetic fields.

On April 27, 1961, a "space telescope" was sent into orbit from Cape Canaveral, Fla. Known as Explorer XI, it travels between 310 and 1,110 miles above the earth. Weighing 95 pounds and shaped like a 7½-foot telescope, the satellite is intended to peer into millions of miles of space in a search for gamma rays, the high energy particles which stream out from various cosmic sources. The satellite will not operate like a conventional telescope. Its front is filled with instruments geared to sort out gamma rays from other space radiations. The data gathered are relayed to earth to be recorded in photographs of wavy lines on an oscilloscope. The satellite tumbled end over end ten times a minute to allow the telescope to scan the entire sky.

A Russian in Space

On April 12, 1961, the Russians scored another "first," perhaps even more dramatic than Sputnik I. On that day the first human, Major Yuri Gagarin, circled the earth in space. The trip was made in 89.1 minutes. He and his ship traveled between 110 and 188 miles above the earth's surface. During most of the journey his speed was about 285 miles a minute.

The space vehicle itself weighed about five tons. It was named Vostok (East). Total time from blastoff to landing was an hour and 48 minutes. The vehicle was controlled by small rockets fired by radio signal from earth. During the flight Major Gagarin is supposed to have talked to his companions, but exercised no direct control over the spaceship. Beyond doubt the flight was one of historical importance, a major accomplishment.

The American Astronaut

May 5, 1961, proved to be a red-letter day for American space efforts, for on that day, after three days of nerve-racking delay because of unfavorable weather conditions, the first American traveled through space. He was Alan B. Shepard, Jr., a 37-year-old Navy commander, one of seven men who had undergone intensive training preliminary to traveling around the earth in orbit. After his ten-foot capsule separated from the Redstone rocket, Shepard hurtled at 5,100 miles per hour through space 115 miles above the earth. The trip lasted fifteen minutes, during which the capsule traveled 302 miles over the Atlantic from its launching point at Cape Canaveral, Fla. Shepard was weightless for about five minutes during the flight. At its conclusion he was picked up by helicopter. The proposed test was publicized in advance, and the flight itself was televised.

Shepard's trip was not as long as Gagarin's: he did not orbit the earth. Nor did he travel as fast or as high. However, he exercised some control over his space ship, which Gagarin did not. He used a periscope to make observations during the flight and he looked out of a porthole: it is not clear whether Gagarin made any observations. A number of instruments were taped to Shepard's body, and these were "read" by radio signals transmitted back to Cape Canaveral. We do not know whether the Russians secured any medical information from Gagarin's flight. The wide publicity surrounding the American test presents a striking contrast to the secrecy surrounding the Russian flight.

A Russian Spends a Day in Space

On July 21 a second American, Virgil Grissom, traveled through space, duplicating the feat of Commander Shepard. But these American space efforts were dwarfed by a second Russian space triumph. On August 6, 1961, Gherman S. Titov, a Russian Air Force captain, took off apparently from the same base east of the Aral Sea from which the first Russian astronaut had gone into orbit. His capsule was reported to have weighed 10,430 pounds — more than twice as much as the American capsules, which weighed 4,500 pounds. Titov, who was promoted to the rank of major while in space, orbited the earth 17½ times and spent 25 hours and 18 minutes aloft. Because of the earth's rotation the extra half orbit was enough to enable Titov to land about 400 miles southeast of Moscow. He had traveled over all six continents and had slept eight hours while in orbit. He had also eaten three meals while traveling the 434,960 miles at a height which varied from 110.3 to 159.3 miles above the earth. In addition he guided his craft, Vostok II, manually and even did setting-up exercises. Except for the period during which he slept he was in constant communication with the earth, reporting his activities and reactions. Apparently all the systems and equipment of the space ship performed their functions well.

The distance Titov traveled was equal to that of a roundtrip to the moon. There is no question that this was an epochal feat and indicated once more the feasibility of travel in orbit around the earth. Travel to the moon or interplanetary travel still pose real problems. However, the Russian successes show that further space conquests can be attempted. These successes also reveal the high quality of Russian science and technology.

The Value of Space Exploration

Of what significance are these various satellites? Are they really important? The Russians have capitalized on their propaganda value. Are they of real significance? Do they make any real contribution to the sum total of scientific knowledge?

The Shape of the Earth

One bit of information which has come from Vanguard I concerns the shape of the earth. For some time it has been held that the earth bulges slightly at the equator. Its shape was believed to be that of a slightly squeezed orange. However, the findings from the Vanguard did not fit with this idea. It was found that the satellite's closest point to the earth was lower in the Northern Hemisphere than in the Southern Hemisphere. This is apparently due to the fact that the earth is slightly drawn up at the North Pole and flattened at the South Pole. Sea level at the North Pole is now thought to be 50 feet higher than was previously believed. On the other hand sea level at the South Pole is 50 feet lower. This discovery is believed to be the second most important finding from the earth satellites to date. The most important has been the existence of the Van Allen radiation belts. Geologists will have to modify their theories as to the make-up of the earth's interior. The core of the earth must be much more solid than was previously thought, even though it may still be a "hot rock" core. In addition, this discovery will play a part in the continuing studies which are being made of the earth's gravitational field.

Space Travel Preliminaries

Successful satellite launchings have brought us nearer to the day of space travel. There are still some very real problems to be overcome. One danger is that of micro-meteors, small bits of matter which may collide like bullets with a space ship. However, the information we have gained from satellites has indicated that this is probably not as serious a problem as it was first thought to be. Both Soviet and American results seem to indicate this.

The Van Allen Layers

A more serious problem is that of radiation. It appears that there are at least two bands of radiation which an astronaut would have to traverse. These are known as the Van Allen radiation belts, named for Dr. James Van Allen of the University of Iowa physics department. These two belts are in the form of rings or doughnuts. Information regarding them has been gained from the various moon rockets and artificial planets. Pioneer III, the unsuccessful moon rocket of the United States, fired by the Army December 6, 1958, traveled 63,000 miles into outer space and reported cosmic ray data almost all the way going outward and coming back earthward.

The two immense electrical doughnuts seemingly trap high energy particles from the sun. The first of these belts is 2,000 miles thick and extends from 1,400 miles above the earth to 3,400 miles above the earth, roughly in line with the equator. The second doughnut is 4,000 miles thick. It begins 8,000 miles out and extends to 12,000 miles. It is thought that these belts are not as intense, or possibly do not exist, at the poles. This is the reason why we are so anxious to get information from a polar rocket. At the present time these belts would make space travel for a human very difficult if not impossible.

Recently another hazard to space travel was discovered. This is the existence of heavy concentrations of protons which have been spewed out from sunspots. They were discovered in the course of a series of balloon flights made under the supervision of several University of Minnesota physicists. It is believed that solar flares or sunspots spray out these heavy concentrations of protons into space. If these sunspots occur in the right sequence, the protons spewed out by one sunspot apparently form a "magnetic channel" by which the atomic particles from the next are sped along through space. It is believed that in long space flights the chances are that a space ship would run into one or more of these proton sprays far out in space.

Moreover, these protons appear to enter the earth's atmosphere most heavily at the North and South poles. If this is correct it might be impossible to launch space flights from the poles, a plan which was suggested to avoid the Van Allen radiation layers. The proton tracks were captured on photographic plates suspended from the balloons.

In order to plan for space travel for humans it is necessary to send animals aloft and study their reactions. The famous dog which was sent aloft in the second Sputnik was a part of that program. In 1958 several Soviet dogs were sent up 281 miles into space and brought back again safely. On December 13, 1958, a monkey was fired into space by the Russians. Later the Russians succeeded in bringing back a number of dogs that had actually been in orbit.

Just as dramatic was the sending of two monkeys into space from the Cape Canaveral missile launching site on May 28, 1959. One of these, Able, was a rhesus monkey weighing six pounds. The second, named Baker, was a one-pound squirrel monkey. Both were female monkeys. Able had been trained to press a lever when a red light flashed. Both monkeys were provided with cushioning to guard them against the shock of takeoff and of re-entry into the earth's atmosphere.

In addition to the monkeys, the nose cone carried tubes

containing living onion tissue, yeast cells, corn and mustard seeds, human blood, and the eggs and sperms of sea urchins. A 60-foot Jupiter missile was used to fire the nose cone into space. A series of transmitters radioed information back. Unfortunately for the original plan, it was necessary to disconnect the button which Able was supposed to press during the flight because it interfered with other electrical equipment.

It was found that the pulse of the rhesus monkey increased from a normal 140 beats a minute to 175 a minute during acceleration. However, during the nine minutes that Able was out in space and was therefore weightless, the pulse was normal and steady. At the time of re-entry the pulse rate rose to 222 — high but not dangerous. Radio contact with the nose cone was maintained for 14 minutes. Then as the nose cone re-entered the earth's atmosphere, contact was lost. Naval vessels were waiting north of Antigua. It was not long until they saw the nose cone re-enter as a bright shooting star. The nose cone with its two passengers was recovered by a naval tug, the *Kiowa*.

Unfortunately Able died a few days later during a routine operation for the removal of the electrodes which telemetered information back to earth. The exact cause of her death is unknown. She may have died as a result of the anesthetic, though she had not reacted unfavorably to the same anesthetic earlier. The electrodes were removed from Baker without anesthetic. She is still alive and will be studied for the rest of her life to determine what effects, if any, the flight had on her.

Studies are also being made on the other materials in the nose cone. The blood was damaged as a result of the flight and could not be used for transfusion. Its corpuscles were ruptured. It is believed, however, that better packaging would prevent this damage to the cells. The attempt to fertilize sea urchin eggs during the flight was unsuccessful. The other materials aboard must still be studied to see what the effects of exposure to cosmic rays will have been. These will have to be grown and then studied.

On July 2, 1959, the Soviets reported that they had sent two dogs and a rabbit to an unrevealed height in a space rocket with a 4,400-pound payload and had brought them back safely. The two dogs were named Darling and Snowflake. According to the Russian statement, this was the third ascent for Darling. In the course of the flight the animals underwent a period of weightlessness and gave new data on the behavior of animals under these conditions. The Soviets reported that these repeated ascents were quite important in obtaining data about the adaptability of animals to flight in rockets. In addition to these three passengers, the Soviet rocket was packed with detection and recording instruments for studying the ultraviolet portion of the solar spectrum. It also contained instruments for determining the structure of the ionosphere, the number of micrometeors, the direction and speed of air currents at different heights, and apparatus for defining the density, pressure, temperatures, and composition of the atmosphere at various heights.

The dogs carried in the Sputniks of 1960 and 1961 were a continuation of these Russian experiments. The United States also continued its studies. On January 31, 1961, a chimp named Ham was sent up from Cape Canaveral, Fla. In a flight of 16½ minutes he experienced seven minutes of weightlessness. Ham was finally picked up by a helicopter, seemingly none the worse for his experience.

The Future of Space Travel

What lies in the future? There is little question but that the exploration of space will continue and will move forward at an increasing rate. The dramatic flights of Gagarin, Shepard, Grissom, and Titov are just a beginning. The National Aeronautics and Space Administration of the Federal Government has developed plans for an American manned-satellite program to orbit the earth. It is known as Project Mercury. The man-carrying capsule as now planned will be in the shape of a cone with a short cylinder attached. Actually it will look very much like a cathode-ray tube. Its base diameter is to be about seven feet. The capsule will probably be made of a nickel alloy or of titanium. It will probably weigh about a ton. It will be designed to withstand any known combination of acceleration, heat loads, and aerodynamic forces that might occur during boost or re-entry. It will have an extremely blunt leading face covered with a heat shield, probably of beryllium.

It is planned to provide the cone with three projecting antennae and a port so placed that the occupant may make direct observations. A couch fitted into the capsule will support the pilot during acceleration. The pressure, temperature, and composition of the atmosphere in the capsule will be maintained within allowable limits for human beings. Food and water will be provided, but this is not expected to be too important because of the short orbit time — 24 hours or less. Medical instrumentation, possibly including a television camera, will evaluate the pilot's response to space flight. Data will be recorded in flight and telemetered to ground recorders.

Other instruments will include a two-way voice radio, instruments to measure and monitor the internal and external capsule environment, and devices to make other scientific observations as space and weight limitations permit. There will be a dual system of control procedures, permitting control of the capsule by the pilot or by the ground station or by both working in conjunction. The pilot himself will have the option of manual or automatic control while the capsule is in orbit.

The capsule will be thrust into orbit by an intercontinental ballistic missile — in all likelihood a modified Atlas. An elaborate escape device is to be provided in case of faulty ignition or improper lifting of the vehicle. It is planned that the capsule should orbit at from 100 to 150 miles above the earth. The escape device will be housed in a frame superstructure which will project from the smaller end of the capsule. It will contain a thin rocket canister. If the launching is successful this will serve to determine the center of gravity. However, if the ground crew becomes aware of any malfunction during ignition and lifting, it can initiate escape procedures by firing the rockets in the canister. These will lift the capsule up and away from the booster. Once clear of the carrier and at a sufficient altitude, the superstructure and the canister will be jettisoned, the parachute which would normally have been used on re-entry, will be drawn out of the short cylinder attached to the cone, and the capsule will return to the surface where an impact bag will diminish the shock of landing.

If the launching succeeds, the satellite will separate from the carrier at the proper altitude, the escape system superstructure and canister will be discarded, small reaction jets will shift the orientation of the long axis of the capsule from the vertical to the horizontal, and the satellite will go into orbit. At any point during the capsule's flight, re-entry and recovery techniques can be initiated by either the pilot or the ground crew personnel. By use of the reaction controls — the small jets placed around the capsule — the path of the container will be changed so that the firing of the retrothrust rockets at the base of the cone will start the capsule back toward the earth. The eventual landing area can be predetermined because of this control over the capsule's point of re-entry into the atmosphere. As the capsule enters the earth's atmosphere once more and slows to a speed approximating that of sound, a parachute will open to stabilize the vehicle. At this point radar chaff — metallic tinsel of the type used for radio jamming — will be released to pinpoint the capsule's location. When the velocity of the capsule decreases to a predetermined rate, a landing parachute will open. The parachute will open at an altitude high enough to permit safe landing on land or water. The capsule will be buoyant and stable in water.

As the manned capsule approaches the impact area it will be the focus of a variety of location and recovery procedures. Control will have been exercised over the timing of re-entry. Ground equipment, probably computers, and capsule equipment will be able to predict the general area of impact. To this information will be added the exact pinpointing made possible by the release of the radar chaff. Triangulation on radio signals from the satellite will offer a supplemental means of location as will visual observation if the re-entry occurs during the daylight hours. Once the capsule is down, recovery aids such as tracking beacons, high intensity flashing light systems, and the two-way voice radio system will be placed in operation. In addition, if the capsule lands in the water, sonar bombs for sending underwater impulses and dye markers will begin operation. If the landing is made in water it is assumed that ships, submarines, and aircraft will be assigned to cover the predicted impact area. Thus recovery of the capsule and its occupant will be virtually assured.

Where will the first astronauts go? Probably the first trips will be simple space voyages from which the earth will be observed. It is hoped that these may be made in 1962. A little later it is planned to make unmanned lunar and interplanetary space probes. A two-man capsule is planned for the mid-60s. A little later it is planned to make a manned lunar probe. Space platforms are also planned. It is believed that the ultimate goal, manned interplanetary flights, will require nuclear propulsion.

Visiting the Moon

In all probability it is the moon that will be first to be visited. Conditions there will probably not only be strange but also inhospitable. Because the moon is smaller than the earth, its gravitational attraction is only one sixth that of the earth. A 180-pound man would weigh only 30 pounds on the moon. Because of its low gravitational attraction the moon is unable to hold much of an atmosphere. In *toto* it is believed to weigh between 10 and 100 tons. The first astronauts landing there will have to take their oxygen along. The moon is also without water, for water evaporates, and water vapor would be lost in the same way that gases are lost. Because there is no atmosphere the sky viewed from the surface of the moon will probably appear to be black, and the stars will be visible at high noon. As the astronauts step out of their space vehicle, all will be calm, silent, and eerie. The wind will not blow because there is practically no air. Moreover, without air there is no transmission of sound. Sunrise and sunset are very abrupt. Temperatures are very hot while the sun is shining and very cold when it is not visible.

The most noticeable features of the moon's surface are visible to us on earth even with the naked eye. They are the so-called *maria,* or seas. They are responsible for the well-known "man in the moon" configuration. Since we believe that the moon is completely without water, we believe they are large plains surrounded by crater walls or mountain ranges. They are not seas. Lunik II landed in one of these.

The moon is believed to contain no life whatsoever. It is also believed to be dead volcanically. However, in the fall of 1958, a Soviet astronomer, Nikolai A. Kozyrev, reported that he had observed what he regarded as a lunar volcanic eruption. He noted a peak which he was observing became blurred and took on an unusual reddish hue. A few hours later this peak was white and bright, but as he continued his observations he noticed a marked drop in the brightness, and the peak resumed its normal appearance. He took several spectrograms, one of which showed the bright light characteristic of an incandescent cloud containing carbon, such as is typical in volcanic eruptions on earth.

A number of astronomers have interpreted his data differently. They believe that he has provided evidence of the existence of a lunar atmosphere composed of rarified gases, something previously not accepted, but they do not believe this necessarily means volcanic activity. It is possible, they believe, that what Kozyrev saw was the leakage of these gases from the interior of the moon.

One of the problems of the exploration of the various extraterrestrial bodies of the solar system is the problem of the possible contamination of such bodies in the initial landings and explorations. Lunik II was sterilized to protect against this possibility. Biological or radioactive contamination could easily occur. This might compromise and forever make impossible critical scientific experiments. The moon's atmosphere is especially vulnerable to contamination, since it is made up of only a small amount of matter. The release of the volatile matter which might be given off by a TNT explosion set off for marking purposes might alter the atmosphere for a very long period of time, since it would probably take some years for the products to escape from the moon's atmosphere. If a flare is to be released it should be of material quite unlike those substances normally present in the moon's atmosphere so that in subsequent investigations it can be clearly recognized as a contaminant introduced by man. It has been suggested that a flare produced by burning metallic sodium in chlorine or bromine should be considered. It is believed that the quantities required to be visible through a telescope would be insufficient to cause serious contamination of the moon's atmosphere. It is hoped that the moon's atmosphere will be studied initially by objects which circle the moon. Once this information has been gained it will be possible to plan landings which will not disturb the atmosphere on the moon or contaminate its surface.

The chemical composition of the dust on the moon's surface is also of considerable scientific interest. This is believed to represent cosmic material which has been captured by the moon in the course of its history. Rocket impact is not too serious a problem. A nuclear explosion would be more serious. This would release volatile fission products which would enter the moon's atmosphere and be distributed rapidly by diffusion. In the near vacuum of the moon even elements like strontium are likely to behave as gases. The radioactive elements released by an atomic explosion will be in a highly reactive form and on coming into contact with moon dust may form involatile compounds. In this way the whole surface of the moon may acquire additional radioactivity which may interfere with subsequent radiochemical analyses of great value in studying the past history of the moon. An A-bomb is likely to do even more damage than an H-bomb in this respect.

There is no danger of contaminating the moon with living cells such as spores of various types and bacteria. These could not give rise to life similar to earth life which might confuse later investigators because of the absence of water on the moon and because of the near vacuum of the moon's atmosphere.

What would be the requirements for a manned base on the moon? As we have already indicated, the base would have to be self-sustaining. The heart of such a system would be a very lightweight electrical generating system. With this system the astronauts could generate heat to set oxygen free from the oxides which it is believed are present on the moon and could release hydrogen from hydrides. The hydrogen and oxygen could then be combined to produce water. Similarly carbon dioxide could be released from carbonates and used in photosynthesis. Advantage would be taken of the high intensity of solar radiation in solar furnaces, solar batteries, and the like. A photoelectric generating system has been developed which consists of a plastic sheet coated with a light-sensitive electron emitter and a wire grid. At the present time its efficiency is too low, but its light weight and the fact that it will function in a vacuum make it an attractive possibility.

Space Travel to the Planets

It appears that the first planets to be explored will be Mars and Venus since they are closest to the earth. Moreover, these two planets are likely to be most like the earth. In exploring them care will have to be exercised to prevent their contamination.

Venus is difficult to study because of its position between the orbit of the earth and the sun. When it is closest to the earth, most of the planet is in shadow and only a thin illuminated crescent can be seen. When it is on the opposite side of the sun from the earth, it is at a great distance from us. It is apparent that Venus, unlike the moon, has a substantial atmosphere. This is evident because its crescent extends much farther than we would expect. Spectroscopic studies have recently been made of the atmosphere. Indications are that large quantities of carbon dioxide — about 500 times as much as on earth — are present in the atmosphere of Venus. No other gases have been identified positively in the Venusian atmosphere. We never see the solid surface of Venus — only the continuous cloud cover. Surface temperatures are estimated to be between 200°C and 300°C. The high temperature of the surface and the scarcity of water and oxygen make it highly unlikely that life as we know it can exist on Venus.

Mars is the nearest planet whose orbit lies outside that of the earth. When the earth and Mars are closest together we therefore see a fully illuminated planet. Even though Mars is smaller than Venus and does not come as close to the earth as does Venus, still it is the planet which we can subject to the most detailed telescopic examination. It is evident that Mars too has an atmosphere. The occasional presence of clouds is an evidence of this. While the solid surface of Mars is usually exposed to visual examination it is occasionally partly obscured by clouds. The one substance that has been identified positively from these clouds is carbon dioxide. It is believed that the quantity of carbon dioxide on Mars is about ten times the quantity on the earth. The existence of water vapor in the atmosphere has long been suspected because of the easily seen white polar caps which wax and wane with the Martian seasons. We are not sure at present whether water really exists on Mars. It is certain that the atmosphere is extremely arid. No bodies of liquid water could exist for any length of time on Mars. It is believed that if there is water present the amount is so small that if it were condensed it would occupy a layer not more than a fraction of a millimeter thick.

Argon is probably present on Mars as is also nitrogen. Indeed most of the atmosphere is probably nitrogen. Temperatures vary a great deal on Mars. The daily range probably exceeds anything we know on earth. When the sun is directly overhead, the temperature may be as high as 86°F. The temperature decreases toward the poles. The summer polar cap has a temperature a little below freezing and the most poleward latitude measurable in the winter hemisphere about —76°F. Nighttime temperatures at the equator are estimated to be about —150°F. These great variations are due primarily to the dryness of the Martian atmosphere which cannot provide a strong "greenhouse" effect.

In the absence of oxygen and appreciable amounts of water, animal life similar to that on earth cannot exist. The various markings on Mars which from time to time have been regarded as evidence of the existence of thinking beings may well be the result of physical phenomena. Dean McLaughlin of the University of Michigan has suggested that the markings on Mars are somewhat analogous to the dust bowls of the Southwest. The absence of oceans and of long mountain ranges permits the trade winds of Mars to pile up drifts and ridges of sand and dust. Because of the lack of oxygen in the Martian atmosphere these may have a greenish tone. Thus both the canals and life on Mars may be illusions produced by Martian meteorology.

Others have suggested that these dark areas of Mars which increase in size and contrast during the summer and weaken in the winter may indicate the existence of bacteria and of elementary plant life. Others have suggested that the green of Mars is actually a neutral gray and may be lava fields. Both this explanation and that of Dean McLaughlin would require the existence of active volcanoes on Mars.

Are there men elsewhere in the universe than on the earth? It is evident that there are no beings with life processes similar to ours anywhere else in the solar system. Astronomers are generally agreed that there is no human life on Mars or Venus and that temperature extremes make life on the other planets impossible. There is no likelihood that we shall be invaded by men from Mars, Venus, or any of the other planets of the solar system. It may be that there is simple plant life on some of the planets though even this may not be the case. We must be very careful not to argue from the Scripture that life cannot exist elsewhere. Scripture is silent on this topic.

Is there life on another planet of another solar system? It may be that we shall never know. To go beyond our own solar system would require traveling with the speed of light. It is unlikely that we shall ever be able to attain such a speed with our space vehicles. Once more we must be careful that we do not argue from the silence of Scripture that life does not exist elsewhere.

Project Ozma

One of the most interesting studies in this connection is being directed by Dr. Frank D. Drake of the National Radio Astronomy Observatory at Green Bank, W. Va. Project Ozma, as it is known, began April 11, 1960. Its purpose is to scan the heavens with an 85-foot radio telescope for evidence of signals being transmitted in space by thinking beings on a planet of another solar system. Listening for such signals was to be carried on for as much as six hours a day. Initially the radio telescope was trained on Tau Ceta and Epsilon Eridani. These are the stars nearest the sun which may have planets which can sustain life. The project involves listening only; there are no facilities for transmitting signals. It was discontinued late in 1960 without any tangible results. The project is to be resumed later.

Is it proper to explore space? Are we not challenging the authority of the Almighty? Certainly the exploration of space is merely an extension of the command given to the Father of us all to subdue the earth. We need not fear that we are flying in the face of God and attempting to wrest from Him information that He would like to keep secret. If there is something that He wants to keep from us, He will certainly be able to put barriers in our way.

Moreover, there is a great deal of good that is likely to come from the exploration of space. We shall learn more about the earth. Already a great deal of information has been gathered which helps us understand and predict weather. The exploration of space is another step forward in man's conquest of his environment. God has commanded us to do this. He has blessed our efforts in the past, and it appears that He is blessing the present efforts that are being made.

THE SPACE AGE CHRISTIAN

chapter

4

THE SPACE AGE CHRISTIAN

What does all this mean to the Christian of the 1960s? How is he to react to these scientific advances? What shall be his attitude over against this thing called science? Certainly his first reaction must be one of gratitude to God for the blessings he enjoys through science. This is a wonderful age to be alive in, a rich age, an age which enjoys unparalleled luxury and ease. The things which make it rich and luxuriant have indeed come through the hand of the scientist, but ultimately they have come from God. And it is to God that the Christian's gratitude must be directed. For one thing, he must recognize God as the Author of these gifts. He must not boast of his own prowess or ability. Twentieth-century science must not be for him another Tower of Babel to challenge the Lord by declaring Him unnecessary. It is God who has worked through modern science. It is God who has unlocked these secrets. The fact that we now know more about how God works in these areas, how the natural laws which He has established operate, does not make God unnecessary. We are still bound by them, and we cannot manipulate them as we see fit.

If there is one lesson which modern science teaches, it is that man must work in harmony with these laws of nature which God has set up. He tampers with them at the risk of doing a great deal of damage. The balances of the natural world are often delicate. The man who attempts to modify them, even with the idea of improving on them, is flirting with disaster. Thomas Austin thought he would improve on nature by introducing rabbits into Australia. He thought he would provide a food which God had forgotten to provide. But he lived to regret his action. The rabbits, without natural enemies, multiplied so rapidly that they became a major scourge.

Nor dare man boast of the greatness of the Babylon which through natural science he has set up. Nebuchadnezzar did this, and the Lord drove him to his knees in madness. God will take His gifts away from those who do not recognize Him as their Author and who do not thank Him. So often such an admonition to gratitude is regarded as the pious mouthing of a preacher. We in America have become especially complacent. We are convinced that it cannot happen here. There is nothing, we believe, that can take away the ease that we enjoy. But as we have pointed out, a nuclear war can take away our prosperity and our ease in the twinkling of an eye. We are not as secure as we were a generation ago. Our two oceans will not keep out the guided missiles of today. Indeed the very complexity of our civilization makes us particularly vulnerable. We are not self-sufficient today, but we are dependent. We take for granted a continuing supply of electricity, gas, pure water, wholesome foods. It is here that we find the Achilles'

heel of America today. For these would disappear overnight were we to have a nuclear war.

Moreover, our very prosperity creates problems in
a world that is filled with havenots. It is still true today
that three fifths of the world goes to bed on an empty
stomach — and that at a time when we in America are
plagued by the problem of surpluses. The hungry are likely
to covet what we have. The riches of America are a tempt-
ing prize.

Certainly the Christian must be grateful to God for these
gifts which he enjoys. And when he expresses his gratitude,
he must also ask God to preserve these gifts to him. The
Lord gives daily bread indeed without our prayer, also to
all the wicked. But our prayer must be that He would lead
us to know it and to receive our daily bread with thanksgiving.

There is another point that must be remembered in this
connection. Americans dare never depend on armaments
for protection. Our ultimate safety does not lie in these,
but in the Lord of hosts. It is so easy to count A-bombs
and H-bombs and guided missiles but to forget to count
God. The Christian cannot forget that real safety is to be
found under His wings.

Encouraging Science and Scientific Research

As Christians living in the 60s we want to be sympa-
thetic to science, to scientific research, and to scientific
problems. We cannot be antiscientific in our attitude and
outlook. Many sincere Christians have at times looked on
science with a great deal of suspicion. This is because science has often challenged traditional thinking. It is true,
of course, that there have been and are scientific theories
which cannot be harmonized with Scriptural revelation. It is
also true that some scientists have became out and out

mechanists and have come to regard God as unnecessary in their scheme of thinking. But it would be a mistake to reject the whole of modern science merely because some of its theories are unacceptable or merely because some of its proponents have rejected God. The scientist is committed to the search for truth. Rarely is he motivated by the desire to upset Scripture and destroy faith. The Christian who has the truth cannot be afraid of scientific research. Such research can but indicate — it cannot refute — the truth of revelation.

Moreover, the great good that has come from science should lead the Christian to encourage it. It has brought evident gifts from God. It must be a tool which He is using to bless us. For that reason, too, it must be encouraged. There is every reason to believe that scientific research will enable us to gain an even greater control over the world in which we live, that we shall more effectively come to subdue the earth and have dominion over it. The history of scientific research has been the history of continuing progress toward that goal.

Using God's Gifts for Good

Probably the greatest challenge that the Christian faces in the 60s is that of using his influence to see that these gifts of God are used for good rather than for evil. God has placed tremendous power into the hands of man. The energy available in the atom is an awesome thing. As we have pointed out, the atom has tremendous potentialities for good. The problem that the atom poses is not one inherent in the atom itself. The problem is in the heart of man. There are those who scoff at the Biblical doctrine of original sin, that ridicule the idea that the imagination of man's heart is evil from his youth. They are quite outspoken in declaring that any such idea has been disproved by the findings of modern psychology. Yet these people unconsciously recognize the correctness of the Biblical teaching by the fears which they express as to the uses to which this new source of energy may be put. The fact of the matter is that we would not be afraid if this new power were regulated by an automaton. We would not be concerned if it were handled by a robot calculator. But we are concerned because it is controlled by human beings, who, though they may be intelligent, are basically selfish, self-centered, yes, basically wicked. This is the real challenge of our age, to show that our generation is worthy to control this power and is capable of using it for good. We need Christianity today more than we have ever needed it before. We need to have the image of the kind and loving Christ imprinted on the hearts of more and more men. We need a special measure of the Spirit in our age so that men who have been made holy through the love of God may reflect that love in the holy lives that they lead. Christianity is not outmoded, not out of date. Scientific developments have made it more necessary than ever before. Science cannot reach into the hearts of men. It has no power to change them. It cannot alter the basic selfishness of human beings. Only the Gospel of Christ can effect that change, so necessary today.

The Christian a Peacemaker

The Christian today must work for peace and pray for peace. There can be no reckless rattling of the sword in the 1960s, no hurling of boastful challenges and dark threats. While we must certainly plan for a nuclear war, it is at the same time unthinkable. We as Christians must do our part to bring better understanding among nations. Often the individual feels helpless in trying to do this. He is but one small person in a nation of 180 million. Yet history is the story of individuals. People long for leadership. They are looking for men and women who will show them the way to international understanding. Our Savior was known as the Prince of Peace. He came to establish the fundamental peace, peace between God and man. His children and disciples must work for peace among men. God does not expect us to give up all planning for our defense. We must protect ourselves against enemies, both real and potential. But at the same time He certainly expects us to work for peace and international understanding.

One way of doing this is to share our scientific know-how and its fruits with others. We can help men by showing them how we do it. But we must not insist that they accept our way of doing things. Nor must we insist that our way of doing things is necessarily the best. If the Chinese, for example, were to use American agricultural methods, three quarters of them would starve to death. The Chinese are able to support a person from a half acre of arable soil. American agricultural methods require two acres to support each person. This does not mean that the Chinese — or any other nation — cannot learn from us. But we must not impose our way of life on them.

We ought also to share the fruits of our scientific progress with other nations. We have become more and more efficient food producers. The result is that our major agricultural problem is one of surpluses. Ought we not share more of these with less fortunate people abroad? No thinking man can be satisfied with our present way of dealing with the problem of surpluses. It is true, of course, that there are real problems even in the distribution of surplus food. Nations have food preferences and prejudices. There is also the problem of transporting these surpluses abroad. But certainly love for our neighbor requires that we seek ways and means of using these surpluses of ours for good.

Christian Love the Answer

Our age calls for a special measure of Christian love. This is true of our attitude toward those outside the confines of our country, men and women who do not enjoy the blessings that scientific advances have brought us. There is also a need for love toward our fellow countrymen. There are bound to be serious economic dislocations in the years that lie ahead as automation, brought about by scientific research and development, becomes more and more common. There is no doubt that with automation we stand on the threshold of a second Industrial Revolution. The first Industrial Revolution was one in which machines replaced men in doing the actual work in industry. Power was no longer supplied by human muscles and by the muscles of animals but by coal. History tells us that the Industrial Revolution was accompanied by serious and substantial economic dislocation. Hand industry disappeared. Men were lured off the farms by the promise of substantial wages in the city. But when they gave up their roots in the soil, they found that they had become dependent on the machines. They were no longer self-sufficient, able to support themselves by their toil on the farm. They had become very dependent. They could no longer feed, clothe, and shelter themselves. They were dependent on others, whose services they could now buy. This was all very fine so long as the factory furnished the wages necessary to purchase the necessities of life. But when the factory shut down, there was no place to turn to secure funds to purchase the necessities of life.

Moreover, industrialization provided many opportunities for exploitation. The services of children were quite commonly used on the farm. Children were a real advantage when men lived on the land. But in a city children became a liability — unless they too could be put to work in the factories. It was not long until exploitation of children became commonplace. They could be paid a pittance and produce almost as much as a man. It was easy to persuade their parents to send them into the factories, for their earnings, though pitifully small, added to the family's income. Women, too, were exploited. When they could not work in the factories, they were put to work at machines that were brought into the home. These two sources of cheap labor — women and children — were used to bring pressure on the heads of households to keep their wages down.

It is quite likely that the second Industrial Revolution will bring about similar dislocations. For today machines are more and more replacing men. The first Industrial Revolution provided machines to take the place of men, but these machines needed men to tend them. Our second Industrial Revolution is supplying machines to tend the machines. Whole factories are run by machines which require supervision by only a small number of human beings. It is obvious that fewer and fewer men will be needed in the factory of the future. What is to become of the men whose places are to be taken by the machines of the second Industrial Revolution? The decreasing work week will supply some additional opportunities for employment. Service industries will no doubt grow in importance. But even with these there is likely to be considerable economic dislocation. We are getting a glimpse of this in the chronic unemployment characteristic of some areas of our country. The coal-producing areas are one example of this. Men who are replaced by machines are finding it almost impossible to secure gainful employment. They are regarded as too old to be trained for new jobs. Yet many of them are in their 40s and 50s, and in the normal course of affairs could expect 15, 20, or 25 years more of gainful employment. This problem, which is being raised by science and scientific progress, requires the attention of the best brains of our country. We cannot shrug it off. We cannot ignore it. We cannot pass by on the other side. Love dictates that we give attention to the problems these people face and that we make an earnest effort to assist them. The problem is particularly important because it is likely to grow.

Providing for the Aged

There is another area in which Christian love will have to show itself more and more. This is in the area of providing for the aged. We are likely to have more and more of them as time goes on, because we are keeping more and more of them alive into the postproductive years. They too face financial problems. If we are not going to permit them to work, we are going to have to provide them with some means of support. But often the major problem of the golden-aged citizen is not a financial one. He needs a feeling of belonging, he needs to feel wanted, he needs to feel useful, he needs most of all to be loved. The Fourth Commandment takes on a new meaning for the Christians who live in the 60s. We cannot say that our obligations to our parents are discharged once we have become adults. They need a special measure of love and affection in their declining years. They ought not be shunted off into an old folks' home arbitrarily. Rather they ought to be cared for and made a part of the family circle. There will be some who will prefer the company of their contemporaries. There will be others who will have no children to whom they can go. There will be still others whose children cannot provide for them and for whom societies and homes for the aged have a need to fill. But to a great many of our golden-aged citizens we owe a home in the family circle.

This is not to minimize the importance of the various organizations which serve the aged. As we have pointed out, they have a real role to fill. They are entitled to our support. As Christians we have an obligation not only to the immediate members of our family but also to all the aging saints. It is this obligation that we discharge by supporting these Christian agencies which minister to their needs, by remembering them in our prayers, and by showing our interest in this work.

The Need for Education

Still another need that science poses is the need for better educational facilities. The citizen of the 60s, 70s, and 80s will have many important decisions to make. They must be made on the basis of understanding and of objective evidence. He must have the facts or at least the means for securing facts. He must know how to distinguish between fact and opinion and must recognize emotional appeals that are made without an objective foundation. The church has always been a friend of education and knowledge. It must be that once more in the 60s. The rapid progress of science makes it necessary that each citizen be provided with the information he needs for making intelligent choices. Not every problem can be decided on the basis of objective data. There will be honest differences of opinon. But the citizen will need as much objective data as he can secure.

Yes, science has raised problems for those of us who are spending our pilgrimage in the space age. There are those who would return to the simpler days when life was not so complex. We cannot do that. Nor would we really want to return to the "good old days." For they were not nearly so good as people represent them as having been. The scientific progress that has been made has by and large been for the good. There are indeed problems to be solved. But with God's help, and acting in keeping with the principles of Christian love, the challenge of the 60s can be met.

INDEX OF TOPICS